JUST BE YOURSELF

JUST
BE YOURSELF

———————— ◆ ————————

By MARY BARD

J. B. LIPPINCOTT COMPANY
PHILADELPHIA AND NEW YORK

For Marion
and all Brownies everywhere
with my love

CONTENTS

JUST BE YOURSELF

1

ESPECIALLY THOSE AT HOME

*L*EADERSHIP of any kind was farthest from my mind on that hazy September morning when Jim and I stood watching our three blonde daughters preparing, each in her own fashion, to leave for the first day of school.

Jim, with a doctor's reaction to his young, beamed impartially on them and said they were nice healthy specimens, weren't they?

I nodded, my mind filled with last minute maternal apprehensions. Now that the youngest was ready for the first grade, had we run aground on the shoals of conflicting child care theories, or were their more obvious failings a question of genes? And if genes, why had they seemed to inherit Jim's sterling qualities and my weaknesses?

Mari, aged nine, was repeating, "Hurry *up!* We'll be *late!*" She was surgically clean, each pleat in her green plaid dress was stiff, her braids were so tight her eyebrows were raised, but—she was harrying her sisters until they were slowing down just to spite her. (I too am the eldest, and I too boss my sisters until they are forced to harden like cement under my showers of advice.)

11

Sally, almost eight, was gazing at the magnolia blossoms as she slowly buttoned her blue plaid dress. She radiated the calm, unhurried serenity of her father, but—her hair was tangled, there was a hole in her sock and she carried her shoes in her left hand. (No matter how long I take to dress, I give the appearance of being slightly out of focus.)

I sighed as Mari switched over to Sally. "Where's your new hair ribbon?"

"I couldn't tie it." Without turning around, Sally opened her fist and disclosed a crumpled blue ribbon.

"I'll bet you didn't even comb your hair!" Grabbing a lock of hair, Mari jerked the ribbon into a bow.

"I didn't. I brushed it."

"There's a hole in your sock," Mari snapped.

"It won't show." Sally squatted down and began to put on her shoes.

Heidi, almost six, was crouched on the front steps holding Cotton, her cat, her arms encircling her two sad-eyed dogs, Dagmar and Spot.

Mari bustled over to her. "Now look. You've got dog hairs all over your new pink dress!"

"Who cares?" Heidi stood up and slapped at the front of her dress. "I don't want to go to school anyway." Jim's devastating honesty but—my dislike of regimentation. (I never could understand why I couldn't grow up in the jungle like Mowgli.)

Mari patted and straightened and marched them ahead of her up the street. Three little girls, dressed alike but as unlike as if they had been spawned by three sets of parents. As they turned at the corner and waved, I had a momentary pang of real angish.

Jim tilted my chin and kissed me. "Never mind. They'll come back."

This prescience is what makes Jim a good doctor, but it also makes it difficult for his wife to have secret thoughts or secret bills. My voice was deliberately bright as I hastily assured him I could hardly wait to rip off the bindweed of babies and begin to nurture my own unhampered growth—

His eyes were amused as he patted me. "Bet you'll begin to hamper before I get home tonight." He grinned. "You might begin by sorting the Medical Journals," and got in the car and drove off, leaving me to wander around the yard in the filtered sunshine trying to visualize what it would be like to have seven uninterrupted hours a day.

Picking up a couple of sweaters, a rusty roller skate and a battered croquet ball from the cluttered racetrack known as "our garden," I walked over and sat down on the edge of the terrace firepit and drew in a long breath of September's heady perfume, a blend of cedar, salt water and lush gardens.

Ours is a lovely city, young and sprawling and covered with tree-studded hills to which her houses cling arbitrarily, hoping they will not let go and slide down into Puget Sound, Lake Washington, Green Lake, or Lake Union. At her head lies Mt. Baker, jagged and white, at her feet rises Mt. Rainier, an aloof pinnacle called by the Indians, "The Great White Father." Occasionally "Father" glances over his clouds at his three adolescent daughters, Tacoma, Seattle, and Everett, and immediately retires again, probably because of their distressing tendency to weep nine months of the year.

Our house braces its feet on the brow of a hill in the central, older portion of town. When we are not suspended in mist, we see a heartlifting panorama across Lake Washington, Mt. Baker, the whole Cascade Range and, now and then, Mt. Rainier. To the north of our house is a ravine which the children regard as their own private forest; to the east a steep bank falls to the street below; to the south there is a large side yard used as a playground by the whole neighborhood because it is the only area which is flat. We face a quiet tree-lined street of old houses and large gardens and conservative people who do not have small children.

We bought the house primarily because of the view and also because it was old, large, inexpensive and just ten minutes from the hospitals. The architecture, if such it could be called, is what is known locally as "early Lumber Baron" or square, three-storied and white. Although supposedly colonial, it actually resembles an enormous refrigerator.

The "old, large, inexpensive," aspect was what I was contemplating as I gazed at rain-streaked windows, peeling window sills and flaking paint.

All three in school! No guard duty! No demands for food! I'd get so much done, Jim wouldn't know the place at the end of a year. The perennial bed, instead of being a starting place for the swing, would be a succession of colorful bloom. The sandbox with its rusty pails, doll dishes and kitchen spoons, I mentally replaced with a neatly bordered rosebed. The terrace was whisked clean of tricycles, bicycles and battered wagons and resplendent with gleaming lawn furniture. Now that I had all day to myself—

The telephone rang. I skidded across the terrace, up the back steps, through the kitchen, into the pantry and grabbed the phone in time to hear, "Where on earth were you?"

It was Susan Blake, a neighbor and boon companion. She continued, "I've just finished giving the house a cold-blooded inspection trip. What've you been doing?"

I gave her a detailed account of our morning's activities, uneasy because I was deliberately starting the game which Jim calls "Cat's Cradle" or the telephonic exchange of threads of gossip, hurts and slights and burdens of housewifely duties, a habit which he says causes more psychosomatic disturbance than money, fears and sex all put together, and finished by asking her if she thought children's behavior was due to faulty upbringing or genes.

"Genes. Definitely. Peggy gets more like Charlie every

day." She enumerated her husband's more irritating qualities which were popping up in her only daughter Peggy.

It was my turn. Jim still had the first Medical Journal
he'd ever received and now he expected me to spend all my
free time cataloguing them—

There was quite a long conversation on what to do with
Husbands' Junk. Susan won by saying she'd thrown away
two old coats and a fishing hat, just as a test, and so far
Charlie'd never even missed them he was so busy organizing
her. "It must be heavenly to have the house to yourself, but
I'll bet you're lonely. Come on now, doesn't the house seem
kind of morbid?"

Not at all. I'd been waiting nine long years for this day.

"Well, what I really called you about is a brand new
menace which is slowly driving me stark, raving crazy. Just
a minute while I get a cup of coffee and a cigarette—"

I looked guiltily at the egg timer Jim had installed to limit
Cat's Cradle to three minutes, went and got my cup of coffee
and my cigarette and picked up the receiver to hear "Girl
Scouts! Peggy is just impossible, and now that school has
started, she'll be worse than ever. You remember when I
let her go to Day Camp—"

I remembered. Mari and Sally had hounded me, but Jim
wouldn't allow it—afraid they'd catch something. Doctors
were so apprehensive, they didn't realize how hard it was to
get anything done when you had small children under foot—

"Men just don't realize. Period. Anyway, ever since Peggy
went to Day Camp, she's been impossible. 'Why can't I be
a Brownie?' morning, noon and night. Honestly, if I hear
that plaint just once more, I'm going to exterminate the Girl
Scouts *and* my only daughter—"

Mari had mentioned several times that she wanted to be
a Brownie, but as she also wanted to be a cowgirl, a ballet
dancer, and a trained nurse, I wasn't too worked up.

As I spoke I saw Mari's green eyes, wide with enthusiasm

as she described some trip the Brownies in her room had taken. I tried to recall exactly what she had said, while Susan told me a harrowing story about the Brownie Leader, an unprincipled female who wouldn't allow Peggy to join her Troop, put her on a nebulous waiting list and then paraded the Brownies back and forth in front of Susan's house, causing screams of anguish from Peggy. "And now, when I'm supposed to be giving the house a thorough fall housecleaning, I've got to start calling the Girl Scout chain of command all over again."

While she enumerated the cleaning miracles she intended to perform before the fall rains set in, I salved my conscience by making a list of the things I was going to do with my seven childless hours a day.

Sort and classify Jim's Medical Journals, cook the things he liked best to eat, repaint the furniture in the girls' rooms, make new slip covers for the living room furniture, new curtains, read Time and Life and the Saturday Review every week so I could talk about something besides housework and children, take regular exercise, return every social engagement, keep up the mending, attend stimulating lectures and concerts . . .

The list was quite impressive by the time Susan said, "It's ten o'clock! I suppose we'd better get to work. Come on down here if you get too lonely—" and hung up.

I opened the door of the refrigerator, noting that as usual the small dishes of unappetizing leftovers did not suggest anything Jim liked best, and caught myself listening for the daily danger signals. The milkman who imperiled Heidi's life by allowing her to ride on the running board of his truck. Roller skates buzzing down the sidewalk. Sally must not skate in the street. A loud, "You put your sweater on right this minute or I'll tell Mother." Were all nine-year-olds as bossy as Mari?

This was utter nonsense. Hadn't I spent the last few

years assuring Jim that I wasn't disorganized, just dormant? The moment all three children were in school, I'd put out so many new shoots he'd have to prune me to keep me in shape.

Why didn't I concentrate on Susan's cold-blooded inspection trip instead of feeling uneasy because the house was so quiet? Susan had said the thing to do was to start at the top and work down, mercilessly discarding everything that was not actually in use.

The third floor, which has a bedroom, bathroom, and six enormous storage closets, is the place we tuck everything we don't know what to do with. Christmas tree ornaments, Easter decorations, outgrown clothes, boxes and boxes of Medical Journals, two pack rats' accumulation of eleven years of marriage. Every box I opened reminded me of some darling thing one of the children had done, which made me so sad I decided to let the attic wait until I was more used to being alone.

Progressing to the second floor, I was reminded of Susan's comment, "Judging by the amount of halls in your house, I should say the early Lumber Barons admired waste space inside as well as out."

I started to sort out the books in our room, preparatory to taking some of them downstairs, but gave up in discouragement because of the teetery stacks of Medical Journals. As a gesture toward the thorough fall housecleaning, I ripped the beds apart and vacuumed the springs, something I'd read about but had never had time to do and which I do not recommend, as it puffs lint all over the rug.

Mari's room was neat but appeared cluttered due to her "collections." Minature dolls, furniture, animals, musical instruments, vases in the shape of everything under the sun but a vase, trading cards, photographs, nothing must be touched or the order of acquisition would be destroyed. I wondered if Mari "collected" because Jim did, or if other nine-year-olds had the same mania.

I opened the door to Sally's room and her large audience of dolls stared disapprovingly as I reached under the bed and fished out the linty panties, socks, shoes and books I knew were there, opened the closet door, and was met by an explosion of clothes. Would Sally ever learn to pick up her things?

Heidi's room was more reminiscent of a pet shop than the boudoir of a dainty little girl. Beside each twin bed was a dog's bed (why, I don't know, because Dagmar and Spot always sleep on Heidi's bed). Hanging on the wall was the parakeet's cage, empty because Squeaky must feel free to divebomb any interloper. On the dressing table was a goldfish bowl containing milky water, viscous plants and three goldfish gasping on the surface and trying to die. Dear Shelley, her turtle, scratched around in another goldfish bowl on top of the bookcase. On the window sill sat Cotton, her cat, switching his tail and hoping Squeaky would come in for a landing close enough to be caught and eaten. I didn't see how the child ever got to sleep with such a loud obbligato of squeaking, panting, snapping, clicking and purring, but it seemed to serve as a lullaby.

After I'd made the bed, cleaned the goldfish bowl, the turtle bowl and Squeaky's cage, I just closed that door.

Down the stairs, along the balcony, down the stairs, dust the entrance hall, the living room (a tube fifteen by forty-eight feet with a telescopic view of the Lake from one end) the den, the dining room, back hall, pantry and huge kitchen. *Why* had Jim and I thought this maze of echoing, empty rooms ideal for a growing family?

There was no use in hurrying. I had days and days, weeks and weeks, years and years. It wouldn't be long before our girls would be grown up, married and gone and the house would always be quiet as the tomb!

By three o'clock I had bathed and changed my clothes, had a festive dinner all prepared, had read two back issues of Time, and felt as forlorn and jumpy as a fire lookout on the farthest peak.

I even had cinnamon toast and cambric tea on the kitchen table when the children came roaring in from school.

Heidi's face was streaked and scarlet and she was bursting with news. "There's a boy in my room and he has a mother rabbit and six baby rabbits and he says I can have one—"

Mari, just as crisp as when she left in the morning, said, "Rabbits. Ugh! Phyllis says—"

Sally, looking as if she'd dived into a clothes basket and rolled out wearing the contents, said dreamily, "There's a new girl in my room named Durdey and she lisps—"

Mari said, "Her name's Dierdre, not Durdey—"

Unperturbed, Sally continued, "Durdey says 'thith' and 'pleathe' and—"

Heidi, who was trying to hug Spot and Dagmar and Cotton all at once, said, "Can I have a baby rabbit, Mother, can I?"

Mari said, "Mo-ther! Phyllis Bean is in my room this year, and she says I might get to be a Brownie. Can I, Mother?"

I beamed at each flushed, excited face, said, "Yes, Heidi, we'll ask Daddy about the rabbit. Yes, Sally, tell me about Dierdre. Yes, Mari, what about the Brownies?" doled out more cinnamon toast and thought, "I love you, I love you, I love you, but by the time you've been in the house five minutes, I don't see why I ever missed you."

Mari banged down her spoon. "Mo-ther! You're not listening. Phyllis says why don't you call Mrs. Burton and ask her if I can be a Brownie? Will you, Mother, will you?"

"Can I have a baby rabbit, can I, Mother?"

"Can I bring Durdey home, can I, Mother?"

"May I" long since having gone down the drain, I said,

"Yes, now let's take turns. Mari, who is Phyllis and what is a Brownie?"

"A Brownie is a Girl Scout—"

Sally clamored, "Can I be a Brownie too, Mother? Durdey is a Brownie—"

Heidi echoed, "Can I be a Brownie too, Mother?"

Mari curled her lip at Heidi. "Take it easy Greasy, you've got a long way to slide."

There were shrieks of appreciative laughter which I dampened with a maternal, "That's not the way to talk."

"It is too. Phyllis says that. Phyllis says their Troop is full, but there might be room for just me. Will you call Mrs. Burton, Mother?" Mari took a slip of paper out of her pocket. "Here's Mrs. Burton's number. Phyllis wrote it down for me. Phyllis says Sally shouldn't come to school with a hole in her sock. Will you get her some clean socks, Mother? Hurry up and change your clothes, you guys, we've gotta play baseball. I'm pitcher—"

They swiped the backs of their hands across milk-rimmed mouths, scrambled up from the table, leaving a trail of crumbs, sweaters, and books and rushed upstairs. Seconds later they were down again leaving, as I well knew, lumps of school clothes on the floor. Mari called, "See you later, Alligator," and shrieking with maniacal laughter, they were gone.

Gone also was my mournful vista and in its place, the familiar irritation. "*Why* do they have to be so noisy and messy and rude?"

I got out the mending basket and began to dig for one pair of matching socks. There must be some secret game children play which involves trading one sock, otherwise how could perfectly good pairs go down the clothes chute and come up a basketful of singles?

So Brownies were Girl Scouts? Why hadn't I listened more carefully to Susan? Oh well, might just as well call

Mrs. Burton and get it over with. I dumped the socks back into the basket and went to the telephone.

Mrs. Burton's voice was warm and friendly. She said yes, Mari was on her waiting list, had been for two years. She was awfully sorry to disappoint me, but her Troop was full and the Council simply would not allow her to have more than sixteen children. No, there weren't any other Troops in the neighborhood. Perhaps Mrs. Lyons, the Neighborhood Chairman, would have a suggestion. She gave me Mrs. Lyons' telephone number.

Mrs. Lyons' voice was also friendly but a little harassed. Not only was Mrs. Burton's Troop full, but she had a long waiting list. She was awfully sorry there was only one Troop in our neighborhood, but she just didn't seem to be able to get anyone interested in being a Leader. So many of the mothers worked. Perhaps the Girl Scout Council would have a suggestion.

The voice at the Council was brisk. Most seven-to-ten-year-old girls wanted to belong to a club and Brownies were a splendid solution. Had I talked to Mrs. Burton? Too bad that Troop was full, she was an excellent Leader. Had I talked to Mrs. Lyons? Too bad she hadn't been able to get more Troops started. The season was just beginning and perhaps there would be some new Troops. Why not call back now and then?

By this time it was five o'clock and the girls came in to get ready for dinner. Mari stood in front of me with her hands on her hips, her face alight with expectation. "What's cookin', Goodlookin'? Did you call Mrs. Burton? What's the word, Bluebird?"

Bluebird hadn't the heart to tell her the extent of the afternoon's research. Instead, I said I was afraid Mrs. Burton's Troop was full, but she was on the waiting list—

Her chin quivered and her eyes filled with tears. "It's just not fair! Phyllis says nobody ever gets to be a Brownie who's on that old waiting list. I'm practically the only girl in our room who isn't a Brownie. Mother, can't you do something?" She burst into tears and rushed upstairs.

Sally fixed me with Jim's direct gaze. "Phyllis won't like Mari if she isn't a Brownie, and she practically runs Mari's room. You'd better do something, Mother."

Heidi put her arms around my knees. "Mari's crying. *You'll* do something, won't you, Mother?"

I said I'd give them their dinner early, and we'd all sit around and have a "discussion."

The discussion is a procedure Jim invented. Under its rules the injured member has the right to take Jim or me into a room, close the door and tattle to her heart's content without interruption. Of course there are bangs and screams and kicks from the other side of the door, but they are ignored. A discussion at which all members of the family are present is usually at dinner, and is in the nature of a council of war.

At this discussion, between shuddering sighs, I discovered that the Brownie mania had been eating away at Mari's heart for some time. It had apparently begun in the second grade and had gathered momentum in the third, until now Phyllis said if Mari didn't become a Brownie this year, it would be too la-a-a-ate!

"But darling, you are on the waiting list—"

"I've been waiting two whole years!"

Feeling like a brutal and inadequate parent, I asked her why she hadn't explained this to me before.

"But I did! I told you and told you, and you always said, 'um-hum' or 'not right now, darling. I'm busy!' But now Phyllis is in my room and I just have to be a Brownie, Mother. I just have to."

Sally and Heidi nodded solemnly at each of these revelations and said, "I told you so, Mother," and I wondered what I *could* have been doing that was more important.

To quiet my conscience, I said, "Now don't give it another thought. I'll do something about a Brownie Troop. You just wait and see."

Sally said Durdey, the one who lisped, was a Brownie and she lived over by the Arboretum and she caught a frog and took it home and her mother was just awful. She screamed and said, "Take it away!" and said frogs were nasty and slimy and made warts. Frogs did not make warts, did they?

Feeling infinitely superior to Durdey's mother at least, I said no, they were useful and interesting but were much happier living with their own frog families in the Arboretum. How, I asked, would they like to be dear little frogs and have a big giant snatch them up and carry them off?

"I wish I had a frog," Heidi said.

"Frogs. Ugh!" Mari said, but the atmosphere seemed to be clearing a little, so I told them a long story about two frogs my sister Betty and I had found once down by the Lake. We took them home and fed them flies and ants and watched them blink their eyes and flick their tongues—

"But I thought you said frogs didn't like to be snatched away by a big giant—" Sally began.

Fortunately the telephone rang.

Mari answered it and came scurrying back to the table red-faced and swallowing. "It's Phyllis, Mother. She wants to speak to you."

Without any preliminary greeting, a flat voice said, "I'm Phyllis. Did you call Mrs. Burton? What did she say?"

She said the Troop was full.

"Did you call Mrs. Lyons? What did she say?"

She said the Troop was full.

"Did you call the Council? What did they say?"

The Troop was still full.

There was a long silence, then the flat voice said, "There's fungus amongus and malaria in the area, let me speak to Mari."

Mari was standing beside me, her face flushed and her eyes intent. I handed the receiver to her and was torn between pride and horror as I heard her say, "Whadya mean, Jellybean? *My* mother'll do something. She always does."

Hearing Jim's car door slam, I told the girls to see who could be fastest at taking a bath and getting ready for bed and as a prize, they could have dessert with Daddy.

Jim came in and kissed me. "Well, how did your first day go? Any new hampers?"

No hampers. Everything was just dandy. Mari seemed to have a new ambition. She wished to be a Brownie, which was of course echoed by the other two, and I'd promised to do something about it but that could hardly be classed as a hamper.

"Knowing your headlong enthusiasm, it will doubtless turn into a hamper. What else did you do?" Jim asked.

He listened amused as I recounted the day's activities, said that it would take me a week or so to get used to being alone all day, and not to get mixed up with Girl Scouts. "I used to be a Boy Scout and looking back on it, it seems to me our Leader must have had the patience and stamina of an early Christian martyr."

No-o-o-o. I had no intention of getting mixed up in it. I'd just look into it. That's all those things required, a little enthusiasm and interest on the part of Mother. It was amazing to me how little interest parents showed in the activities of their children away from home.

Jim said, "Hamper, hamper, hamper. Don't get mixed up in it. What have we got for dinner? I'm starved."

The girls came bounding down, looking like three damp pink angels, fell on Jim and all began to talk at once about the Brownies.

Even hot apple pie did not prevent him from wincing at "What's your trouble, Bubble?" and "Right on time, Slime." But I was so busy thinking about the "something" I had promised to do, that I allowed the trackless wastes of Phyllis' humor, Durdey's lisp and Johnnie's rabbits to go on and on and on.

When the girls had gone to bed, and we were sitting on the porch enjoying the pink glow on the mountains, Jim remarked that after the singularly dull conversation at dinner, it might be wise to concentrate on ways to dispose of Phyllis rather than on Brownies which would merely serve to cement this new friendship.

I said airily that this was the first day of school, and Phyllis would no doubt be supplanted before the week was out.

I was wrong. From then on, "Phyllis says" became the order of our days and nights. I was grateful when Phyllis said that the girls were to pick up their clothes, make their beds neatly, and clean up their rooms before they left for school. But cooler when apples were snatched out of my hand, "Phyllis says this is the way to peel an apple so you won't cut yourself or waste the apple." If I protested even faintly, all three turned on me, "Mo-ther-r-r-r! Phyllis is just trying to help us be Brownies!"

Phyllis also said that Mari was to hand Daddy the paper and his slippers every night when he came home. Daddy, exhausted by an accumulation of whining patients, was grateful to receive a folded paper instead of being forced to wrench it away from three recumbent funny paper readers, but less enthusiastic when requested to read aloud and explain news items. "Da-a-a-addy! Phyllis' father always does!"

Each afternoon Phyllis called me, "Did you call Mrs. Burton? Did you call Mrs. Lyons? Did you call the Council? Mari said you were going to do something. What are you doing?"

Friday afternoon I went up to Murphy's Market to buy the week end's supply of groceries and discovered that ours was not the only house that was Phyllis-infested.

Murphy's Market is the heart of our small shopping district. Originally an old-fashioned grocery store, additions and storerooms have been tucked on until it resembles a freight train on a curve. Murphy's is also the gathering place where we all shop and gossip and keep track of one another's vital statistics. Vi presides, a huge, pink-and-white pastry of a woman who knows everyone in the district and who is kindness personified. Murph, Vi's husband, is a small wiry man who is passionately interested in everyone's problems but his own. Haze, the bookkeeper, sits in a cuckoo's nest suspended over the back of the store, fretting over Murph and calling out at intervals to the customers below, "Better watch it, bill's pretty high." Dave, a lean exhausted butcher, who feels personally responsible for the low grade and exorbitant price of meat, has a shop across the back of the store and spends most of his time comforting the housewives with new ways to cook hamburger.

Talking to Vi is confusing until you get used to it, as if you were listening to a radio serial and stock market quotations simultaneously.

I pushed my laden basket into the slot and Vi said, "I hear Mari wants to be a Brownie, TWO FOR TWENTY-NINE, yeah, Phyllis Bean was in here, funny kid, SEVENTY-ONE A QUART, too bad there aren't more Troops, FIFTEEN, TWO FOR A QUARTER, the kids around here really need it, ABOVE THE DUTCH CLEANSER, MURPH, most of the mothers around here work, kids run the streets." Vi's deep voice rose another notch, "Hey, Mrs. Allen? Weren't you girls talking about the Brownies? YEH THOSE ARE THE ONES, THEY'RE NOT FLORIDA BUT THEY'RE SURE SWEET, come on over here and let Mrs. Jay in on it—"

A clutch of neighbors pushed their carts toward the check stand and a Greek chorus of complaints arose. Vi handed each of us a sample of cheese, leaned her plump arms on the counter and listened.

"Perfectly ridiculous for Mrs. Burton to have a waiting list—this district could support at least five more Brownie Troops—one teacher said she wasn't going to allow the Brownies to wear their uniforms to school, it caused so much unhappiness—if only Phyllis Bean didn't stir them up all the time—"

Vi banged the cash register and comforted each one in turn. "Now, Mrs. Allen, with all the kids in this district, Mrs. Burton's gotta have a waiting list. But Mrs. Schwartz, a lotta the mothers around here gotta work. They've gotta eat don't they? Since when did teachers care what kids wore to school? You can't blame Phyllis Bean for talking, she's a real proud Brownie."

The complaints died to muttering and Vi said, "It's tough when they can't go home after school. Murph does all he can," she pointed to the mourner's bench in the corner where a dozen or so children, ranging in age from three to twelve, sat reading comics and eating apples. Her voice lowered to a husky whisper, "Every day they come in here to wait. Sometimes as many as fifteen or twenty. Locked out. We give 'em an apple or a cookie and let 'em use the toilet and Murph keeps that box of comics for them to read, but gosh, they shouldn't be hangin' around the corner waitin' for their moms to come home from work." She shook her mound of butter-colored curls. "NO, THOSE ARE JONATHANS, DELICIOUS IN THE NEXT BIN—"

All that week end as I shouted, "Don't skate in the street, Sally," "Mari, you'd better put your sweater on," "Heidi, let me look at you, are you catching cold?" I wondered what happened to children of working mothers. It took all my wit and ingenuity to guard ours and keep them amused. What if they had no one to look after them?

Monday afternoon I made elaborate gingerbread men in

a vain attempt to make up to our daughters for not being Brownies and was just taking them out of the oven when the girls came home bringing with them a stocky child with short, tan braids, tan eyebrows and eyelashes and a tan, snubnosed face. She was clad from head to toe in light brown, and she just stood in the kitchen doorway and stared at me through round horn-rimmed glasses.

Mari pulled her forward and said proudly, "Mother, this is Phyllis. She wants to see you."

Phyllis said, "How-do-you-do" and stared unblinkingly at me as I asked her if she would like to sit down and have tea with us.

Shaking her head, she walked solemnly all around me and looked me up and down. Then she turned and stalked out the back door, calling over her shoulder, "See you later, Alligator" and was gone.

"What was that for?" I asked.

Mari said, "Phyllis walked clear home with me to see what you were like," Sally added. "She has to hurry, she's going to the Brownie meeting," and Heidi said, "The lucky pup." They pulled out their chairs and sat down and looked sadder and more forlorn than ever as they chewed the heads off their gingerbread men.

Jim came home early that night, an event that is sufficiently unusual to cause a mild celebration in the way of a family dinner. Instead of entertaining him by gasping out tales of cruel teachers, sadistic classmates and schoolwork that was so hard not one child in the room could do it, they pushed their food around, quoted Phyllis, sighed heavily and whined, "Why can't we be Brownies?"

I too was toying with my food. This was no passing phase. This had lasted a week and gave every indication of lasting all winter. Mist into drizzle, drizzle into rain, rain into steady downpour *and* Brownies? Oh no.

Jim said, "This seems to warrant a family discussion. Mari, suppose you begin."

Mari folded her hands and in Phyllis' flat voice said, "Well! A Brownie is a Girl Scout. When you're a Brownie, Phyllis says you have to promise to love God and your country and to help other people, especially those at home."

"Sounds worth while," Jim said. "What else?"

"And then, when you're ten years old, you Fly Up and turn into a Tenderfoot Girl Scout, but first you have to know the ten Girl Scout Laws—"

"I do—" Sally held up her fingers and counted off, "A Girl Scout's honor is to be trusted. A Girl Scout is loyal. A Girl Scout's duty is to be useful and to help others. A Girl Scout is a friend to all and a sister to every other Girl Scout. A Girl Scout is courteous. A Girl Scout is a friend to animals. A Girl Scout obeys orders. A Girl Scout is cheerful. A Girl Scout is thrifty. A Girl Scout is clean in thought, word, and deed."

"Mo-ther-r-r! She's not supposed to know the Laws!" Mari wailed.

Sally shrugged. "I can't help it. Phyllis says them all the time."

Heidi said, "Phyllis says Brownies can have all the animals they want. Can I have a baby rabbit, Daddy?"

Jim roared, "NO!" and Heidi began to bawl.

Mari's mouth was working. "I'm practically the only girl in our room who doesn't go to the Brownie meeting on Monday. I have to walk home alo-o-o-o-ne—" she began to bawl.

Sally looked straight at Jim. "Daddy, you're not one bit fair. Phyllis says most Daddies *want* their children to be Brownies—" she began to bawl.

Jim threw down his napkin. "Either they're Brownies, or I'm going to eat all my meals in the den."

2

JUST BE YOURSELF

UESDAY afternoon I drove downtown to the Girl
Scout Council (where I should have gone two years before
when Mari first said she wanted to be a Brownie). Each
street end framed a charming landscape; furry green islands
wreathed in tendrils of mist; orange stacked freighters slip-
ping through the Sound toward the ocean; a sunrift high-
lighting a crystalline peak in the Olympics. Water to swim
in, mountains to climb, parks in every direction—Girl Scouts
were all very well for children in overcrowded areas, but in
a place like this?

The Council was a beehive of activity. Brisk women were
typing, telephoning, writing on cards, and sorting pamphlets.
Shelves were swaybacked with books and catalogues. Stacks
of forms covered every available surface and overflowed in
teetery pyramids onto the floor. Walls were plastered with
posters of healthy clear-eyed children proudly saluting the
flag, paddling canoes, saving lives, skiing, building fires,
cooking, cleaning—everything but whining, "Why can't I be
a Brownie, Mother?"

A young woman in a green uniform was rubbing the back

of her neck and staring at the ceiling as she talked sooth-ingly into the telephone, "I'm sorry. That Troop is full. Have you talked to your Neighborhood Chairman? You might call us from time to time. 'Bye."

This familiar chant did nothing to soothe me as I stood at the counter feeling, and no doubt looking, not unlike a female grizzly whose young are threatened.

The green-clad young woman slid back her chair, stood up and came over to the counter. "Good afternoon. I'm Pat Smith. May I help you?"

I said yes. I had come to headquarters to see if there was any valid reason why the Girl Scouts couldn't absorb at least one more Brownie.

"Oh yes. Will you come into my office?"

I followed her down a hall and into an office papered with even larger, more active posters. Over her desk were framed copies of the Brownie Promise and the ten Girl Scout Laws which had precipitated my visit.

My reaction to these documents was maternal rather than rational. *If* Girl Scouts were so trustworthy, loyal, useful, friendly, courteous, kind to animals, obedient, cheerful, thrifty, and clean minded, *why* didn't they do something constructive about all the little girls who were wistfully peering through the Girl Scout fence?

Even before I sat down, I began. Why did a huge na-tional organization allow groups of little girls to go around making other little girls green with envy when the organiza-tion, by its own admission, was already so overcrowded it couldn't take in one new member? In our neighborhood the Brownie disease had reached epidemic proportions. Every girl seemed to be infected and the cure was unavailable. For all the Girl Scouts knew, they might be causing per-manent psychic trauma—

Pat Smith interrupted soothingly to ask for my name and address and the names and ages of our children.

She watched me as she filled out some cards and when she saw that my nostrils had stopped quivering, asked what I knew about their program.

I said that as far as I had been able to discover, it consisted of various indifferent voices on various telephones, and one flinthearted leader named Mrs. Burton, who refused categorically to take more than sixteen children into her Troop. By her own admission she had a long waiting list, and yet she allowed her Brownies to torment the other children—

She took a card out of a file on her desk, tapped her front teeth with a pencil and shook her head. "You've talked to Mrs. Lyons of course—"

I had. Along with other mothers in our neighborhood, I had called Mrs. Burton, Mrs. Lyons and the Council until I was hoarse. I said a lot more in that vein and ended by asking, "Is there any valid reason why there aren't more Troops?"

"Yes. We can't get Leaders." Leaning forward she gazed at me with steadfast hazel eyes. "Have you ever considered being a Leader?"

Heavens no! I had no qualifications and anyway my husband didn't want me to get mixed up in it.

She sighed. "Mrs. Burton is working under difficulties. She has a very small house, is pregnant, and I'm sure she would be grateful for any help, particularly if you would offer to have an occasional meeting. Have you thought of inviting her Troop to meet at your house?"

I flushed and admitted that the thought had occurred to me, but with a long waiting list, I felt the offer might smack of bribery.

She shook her head. "Not if you're willing to help— Have you ever been a Girl Scout?"

Never, but then I'd had an unusual childhood. My father was a mining engineer and we traveled constantly. We seldom spent more than six months in one place and were therefore forced to fall back on the resources of a large family for companionship.

"Too bad. You missed a lot." She turned on the full battery of her healthy personal magnetism. "I'm your District Director. Suppose I begin by telling you something of our program. It is designed to meet the needs of three age groups. Brownies, who are girls from seven through nine, Intermediate Girl Scouts, from ten through thirteen, and Senior Scouts, from fourteen through seventeen. Each age level has its own activities geared to capacity and interest, but we follow the same basic program throughout, to help them to help themselves, to help others.

"Let's see, Mari is nine. She's beginning to be responsible, reasonable, fair-minded and dependable. She's neat, but she's also critical, particularly of her younger sisters. Right?"

I burst out laughing.

"Now wait. Sally is eight. She is vague, tells tall tales, asks for praise constantly, starts to do things but seldom finishes, and everything in her room is stuffed under the bed. Right?"

I couldn't believe she didn't know them.

"I'm not too good at Heidi, but I can tell you what she's going to do next year when she's seven. Come on now, what made you come down here? Phyllis Bean?"

I began by giving her a thumbnail sketch of Phyllis' destructive influence on our relatively peaceful existence, and then, because she seemed sympathetic and genuinely interested, found myself pouring out the problems of a doctor's wife who not only has all the conflicting theories of child care to contend with, but also is beset by the latest medical theories before they've even jelled.

She patted my shoulder. "You love your children and that's the main thing. We see all kinds and we know they can weather anything as long as they know you love them.

But about Phyllis—" She told me of several trips Phyllis had made down to the Council to complain about the waiting list and the way they were running things. "By the way, she also told us that she'd called on you and you had a big house and you might turn into a Leader."

Before I had a chance to react to this blow, Pat Smith said, "Believe it or not, I used to be a lot like Phyllis. Not quite so uninhibited as to behavior but every bit as fanatic." She leaned back in her chair and launched into a graphic description of her own antics as a dedicated Brownie, as an Intermediate Girl Scout determined to win the most proficiency badges (at this point she interjected, "And winning badges is *not* the point," quite sternly), and as a Senior Scout. "By that time I was out to save the whole world, believe me." She shuddered. "When I look back on it, I don't see how my mother ever stood it."

These tales were interrupted constantly by the telephone. My original antagonism toward the Council melted into sympathy as I heard her sigh and repeat over and over again, "I'm sorry. That Troop is full. No, we cannot recommend a larger Troop."

"Why can't you recommend a larger Troop?" I asked.

"You can't do justice to a larger group of children—I'm sorry, that telephone—"

While she was talking on the telephone, she handed me charmingly illustrated pamphlets and catalogues of earnest little girls, just like ours, sewing, drawing, examining bugs and plants, even pleasantly helping "those at home."

Then she switched into a discussion of our district. Old houses converted into apartment houses, overcrowded living conditions, a large Negro area, many nationalities, working mothers, which meant that children were left pretty much to their own devices.

"Of course, Troops in your district are more interesting

than in areas where there is less financial inequality. The children are more appreciative. But there are fewer mothers with leisure time to give to their children."

It was beginning to dawn on me that Leaders were merely mothers and that I might even qualify, eventually, when Pat Smith stood up, "I'm awfully sorry to interrupt this pleasant visit, but I promised to attend a Scout ceremony this afternoon. A Brownie Troop is Flying Up and turning into Intermediates. I wouldn't miss it for anything. Just wait until your girls Fly Up, you'll see what I mean."

Her assumption that our daughters were going to be Brownies cheered me to such an extent that I said I just hadn't realized what they were up against. It was amazing to me that more mothers were not willing to help. Poor little Mrs. Burton! Imagine being pregnant and trying to handle sixteen children! It was all I could manage to handle three. If there was anything I could do to help—

She took my hand in a firm grip. "Good! I'll take care of it." She grinned engagingly. "See for yourself what fun it is. You'll find Brownies are children just like yours, and what is far more interesting, yours are just like all the others. By the way, you might pick up a Leader's Guide. But when you read it, remember, the most important thing is—just be yourself!" She waved me confidently out the door.

Being myself, I stopped on the way home and bought a Leader's Guide. Leafing through it while I was waiting for my change, my enthusiasm mounted to a white heat.

All the way home I had visions: Mari at the tiller of a sailboat, her Mariner's cap at a jaunty angle; Sally gazing into the firelight as she sang around a campfire; Heidi, rigid with excitement as she jogged along on a pack horse. Not only would I call Mrs. Burton the moment I got home, I would ask her to have the very next meeting at our house.

I opened the front door to be greeted with shrieks of joy.

Mari threw herself into my arms. "Mother! Mother! Guess what! Phyllis called and I can be a Brownie, and they're going to have a meeting at our house and Sally and Heidi can come too. Isn't that neat?"

It was. It was the neatest trick of the week.

3

BROWNIES ARE HUMAN BEINGS

$\mathscr{A}$LTHOUGH my first Brownie meeting was a howling success, there would have been less howling had I heeded the Leader's Guide's warning, "Brownies are not cute, adorable children. They are human beings."

The night I came home from the Council and called Mrs. Burton to confirm Phyllis' kind offer, she said she was *so* glad to have Mari in the Troop, and she certainly appreciated being able to use our gameroom.

"What about Sally?" I asked hopefully.

Well, most of her girls were in the fourth grade and she thought we'd better wait until some of them Flew Up. The Council warned that sixteen children was all any Leader could handle successfully, but of course Sally and Heidi were welcome to attend the meetings at our house.

She continued, "Pat Smith says you'd probably prefer to start as my assistant leader rather than take a Troop of your own right away. I'm so glad, because my assistant has taken over our girls who Flew Up last year, and I just don't seem to have the oomph I used to have now that I'm pregnant."

My oomph was rapidly oozing away. Here I was practically an assistant Leader and I'd never even seen a Brownie with the exception of Phyllis, which was hardly reassuring. But Mari was hopping excitedly on one side of me and Sally was breathing heavily on the other side and Heidi was leaning against my lap, so I assured Mrs. Burton that she could use the gameroom whenever she liked. But perhaps I'd better remain unofficial, at least until I had attended one meeting.

She laughed and said Mari could come along with Phyllis on Monday, and she'd let me know when the meeting was to be at our house.

When Jim came home Mari clung to his legs crooning, "I'm going to be a Brownie, I'm going to be a Brownie," while I inundated him with extravagant tales of my visit to the Council. Pat Smith was marvelous—clairvoyant about children—so young and dedicated—if only he could have heard her stories—imagine having trouble getting Leaders— mothers ought to compete for the privilege—

Jim took my chin in his hand. "I judge you won that privilege—"

No-o-o-o. I'd just offered to help Mrs. Burton, poor little thing!

We were just sitting down to dinner when Phyllis called and demanded to talk to me. "I called Miss Smith and Mrs. Lyons and Mrs. Burton and everything is all fixed. Now you'll have to go downtown tomorrow and buy Mari a uniform and all the stuff that goes with it. You'll have to get yourself a Games Book so you'll know how to play. 'Bye."

I came back to the table to hear Sally say, "—but Durdey is a Brownie and she's only eight—"

The next afternoon we went downtown to buy Mari's equipment. Phyllis had given her a list of the prime necessities. Cap, dress, socks, purse, sweater, T shirt, shorts, Brownie Handbook, and GAMES FOR GIRL SCOUTS for Mother.

Mari pranced in front of the mirror in raptures which reduced Sally to tears and Heidi to sulkiness which no amount of "You just wait. Pretty soon it will be your turn," could allay. While our purchases were being wrapped up the young and inexperienced clerk told us she really was not supposed to sell us the equipment until Mari was a registered member of a Troop. It was a Girl Scout rule. "It means something too," she added. "That uniform isn't just a dress . . . I was a Brownie myself, so I know." She knew I didn't want to make another trip downtown so she'd let us take them, but Mari was not to wear her Brownie dress or cap until she was registered. Mari was crushed, but I must confess I was charmed to find the omniscient Phyllis wrong on one point.

Monday morning Mari left for school carrying her purse and wearing her sweater and socks and threatening to tell Phyllis on that mean lady at the store. When she came home at five-thirty, she was an authority on the entire Scout movement. She switched around bossing all of us and quoting Phyllis. "Here, let me do that. Here, let me help you. No, that's not the way—"

Heidi was philosophical. "Okay, Smarty. If you and that old Phyllis know so much, do it yourself." But Sally eagerly tried to do just as Phyllis had said, meanwhile following me around with mournful blue eyes. "*When* can I be a Brownie, Mother?"

At dinner Jim deliberately put his head in the noose by asking Mari to tell us about her meeting.

She patted her sweater. "Phyllis is president—"

"So I judged—" Jim said.

"—and first we have opening. Then we have minutes—"

Heidi jeered, "Aw, you and your old minutes. Everybody has minutes—"

"Not that kind of minutes, dumby—"

The rest of Mari's account was so full of enigmatic references that Jim said it reminded him of the good old days in the Navy.

She finished with, "Oh, I almost forgot. Phyllis says you have to learn to play our songs, Mother. She says for you to be sure and get a SING TOGETHER."

"What's a Sing Together?" Sally asked.

"It's a Girl Scout Song Book in case you're interested," Mari said loftily.

They were so interested they stuck out their tongues and hissed like snakes.

Jim said, "Would it be possible to allay this sibling rivalry somewhat, by a gentle horse trade?"

There was an immediate silence as we tried to figure out what Daddy was talking about.

Jim continued, "I hesitate to employ pressure, but would this *enceinte* director be willing to accept further responsibility if we threatened to withdraw our shelter?"

I said I doubted it. She seemed to have a fixation on the number "sixteen."

"It couldn't worsen the situation to try." Jim nodded toward Sally who hadn't eaten one bite of her dinner and was staring enviously at Mari's sweater and purse from which she refused to be parted. Two large tears spilled down Sally's cheeks and splatted on her plate.

Mari watched her, wriggled and squirmed, looked first at Jim and then at me and said, "It's just not fair. I don't even want to be a Brownie, if they don't want my sister."

"What about me?" Heidi asked.

Sally and Mari chorused, "You're too young, Dopey." But Jim said why not clear this thing up once and for all by warning Mrs. Burton that in our family, it was all or nothing.

After the girls were in bed, I called Mrs. Burton, intending to use the velvet glove but to leave no question in her mind. No Sally—no gameroom. Before I had a chance to begin the usual female sparring, she said she was glad I called because she was just going to call me. Phyllis had stayed after the meeting to point out that Sally was almost eight years old and it wasn't fair to take one sister without the other. She did hope that the Council would not have a fit, sixteen was the absolute limit, but she did have a couple of girls who thought they were going to move away and please, please, not to mention it to one soul in the neighborhood.

Limp with relief, I sat right down to read the Leader's Guide from cover to cover. It seemed to contain everything the mother of small girls wanted to know, as well as several dire warnings about overcrowded troops, which I determinedly ignored. I became so absorbed that when our daughters called, "Mo-ther-r-r! When are you going to kiss us goodnight?" I yelled, "For heaven's sake KEEP STILL!" and then hurriedly dropping my voice to a Leader's dulcet tones, caroled, "Mummy is reading about the Brownies!"

I had just reached, "A nine-year-old is quite a person" when the phone rang.

Jim answered it and came back into the living room shaking his head. "That was Phyllis. She seems to have radar beamed to our house. She says not to forget to go downtown and buy Sally's outfit and not to forget to buy a Sing Together so you'll know how to sing their songs. I wonder what we ever did before we knew Phyllis."

He came over and sat on the couch beside me. "Now look here, this Brownie business is all very well. It would be a good idea to have the meetings in the gameroom, might give the girls an incentive to play down there. You're used to children and I daresay you'll enjoy it, but there's no sense in allowing it to dominate our lives. What about that list of things you were going to do as soon as the children were all in school?"

Oh, it was coming along gradually. At least the summer

clothes were all washed and put away and the storage closets were cleaned—

Jim smiled, "—and the stairs are mined with boxes over which one of us is going to trip and break a leg—"

I had intended to take the boxes down to the basement, but I had been so busy answering the telephone— "I don't see why doctors' wives are expected to be on every committee in town. Taking care of small children is far less hampering than time-wasting committees—"

Jim put his arm around me. "There is a fairly simple remedy to all of your problems, but I doubt if you'll use it—"

"What simple remedy?"

"Just put your tongue against the back of your teeth and follow that by an 'o' sound, n-n-n-no! Try it."

I did try it and it worked fairly well with the importunate committee chairmen, but not so well with Phyllis. She called before and after dinner until I finally gave in and took Sally, and of course the other two, down to buy Sally's equipment. Cap, dress, socks, purse, sweater, T shirt, shorts and a SING TOGETHER for Mother. It was Sally's turn to stand in front of the mirror speechless with joy while Mari jerked and patted and bossed. This time we had an older clerk who refused to allow us to take home the Brownie dress and cap. Mari flew at her like an enraged bantam chicken, but she was firm. "I'm sorry, but those are the Girl Scout rules and we have to follow them."

By this time Heidi's bitterness had reached such depths, she said, "Okay for you then. I'll never buy a Brownie dress, no matter how much you beg me." (And she never did.)

Monday mornings were rent with shrieks of "Mother, where's my—" After frantic searching on the part of the whole family, sweaters were buttoned, purses were clutched, and Mari and Sally strode proudly off, followed by Heidi in whatever hand-me-down she'd happened to run across while dressing.

By the first week in October I had cleaned my way dog-gedly down to the first floor, nobody could find anything, and frankly the house looked pretty much as it had before I started Susan's thorough fall housecleaning.

Jim got so tired of leaping over boxes to answer the telephone that Sunday he decided to head a family project to "get things in order around here." He threw away, and the girls snatched back, until he finally sent them bawling up to make their rooms "surgically clean" and came out to help me with the kitchen.

Our kitchen has eight-foot ceilings, windows on three sides, yards and yards of linoleum-covered working surfaces and so many cupboards and drawers I put things away and don't run across them for months. While I rummaged in drawers and said, "I wonder what I bought this for," Jim stood on an unsteady ladder scrubbing the paint off the ceiling and describing how immaculate hospital kitchens were.

By suppertime the boxes were down in the basement, the girls' rooms had been "inspected," the kitchen was gleaming, and we were all so grumpy, Jim offered to take us out to dinner to cheer us up.

Monday morning at breakfast we were listening to Jim tell how simple it was to keep a kitchen immaculate when Mari casually announced, "Phyllis told me to have our Brownie meeting here this afternoon. I just said, 'Heavens! Don't have it at our house. My mother's cleaning and she's crabby as the dickens.' They're coming anyway."

I said, "Why on earth didn't you tell me—"

Sally said, "We did. We told you last Monday and you just said, 'Sure, sure, anything as long as you don't get into those boxes—'"

Mari said, "Don't forget to make cookies and lemonade. It's my turn to furnish the treat—"

Jim cleared his throat. "Perhaps this is not the day to

bring the medical speaker home for dinner. I've already asked him, but we could just as well go to the club—"

I promised everybody I'd do everything and shoved them all out the door and sat down with a second cup of coffee to call Mrs. Burton and see what I was supposed to do as unofficial assistant Leader.

She said nothing, absolutely nothing. They handled their own meetings. She had an appointment with the doctor and might be a little late. "I'll do my best to get there, but you know doctors."

I rushed through the breakfast dishes, slapped up the beds and went down to the gameroom to pick up the toys and lay a fire. I hadn't been down there all summer and the sight that met my eyes made me realize just why the children complained when I sent them to the gameroom to play.

It was dank and cold. The ceiling pipes, which presumably heated the room, were festooned with spiderwebs and barely lukewarm to the touch. The bookshelves, on three sides of the room, were filled with an accumulation of broken toys, old magazines, dress-up clothes and junk. A jack-o'-lantern leered from a corner of the mantel. The windows, opening on cement light wells, framed piles of dead leaves. The only light in this misnamed playroom was provided by two standing lamps with crooked shades. The furniture consisted of a shabby wing chair, two wicker chairs and a long table with a bench on each side which had formerly been a picnic table.

"If the Council saw this, they'd hale me into court for criminal neglect," I thought as I put 150-watt globes in the lamps instead of the 25-watt I'd casually handed the children. The resulting glare exposed a nest of mildewed cookies in one corner and several sticky coke bottles in another. I burned most of the litter in the fireplace which made the room almost warm, cleaned out the light wells from the inside, scrubbed the shelves and table and had just decided to do it all over again, this time with disinfectant, when the phone rang.

It was Susan. "I haven't heard from you for days. What have you been doing?"

I'd been helping Jim make the kitchen surgically clean and was now working on the gameroom which I had not entered all summer. Not only that, but Jim was bringing guests home for dinner and the Brownies were meeting at our house—

"WHAT?"

Well, yes. As a matter of fact I'd been intending to tell her, but Mrs. Burton made such a fuss about my not mentioning it. I'd offered the gameroom for meetings, so Mari and Sally could join the Troop.

There was a long silence. Then Susan said, "Anybody who is sneaky enough to jump a waiting list deserves to have guests and Brownies on the same day. Guess what? I've just finished making a batch of bread."

Knowing that Susan loathed to cook, it was my turn to say, "WHAT!"

"Remember how we used to make it during the war? There is nothing Peggy loves as much as fresh bread—"

The neighborhood children loved it so much I'd stopped making it. They popped up out of the ground the moment they smelled it baking and stood in front of me with twitching noses and grubby hands begging for hot bread and butter.

"I always try to cook something special when I'm housecleaning, sort of a sop to Charlie when everything's in a mess. Why don't you stir up a batch? I'll bet the Brownies would love it."

I hung up the phone and went right out to the kitchen and stirred up a double recipe, thinking as I measured the flour how patient Jim had been and how he loved to come home to a cozy house filled with the warm fragrance of freshly baked bread and how proud Mari and Sally would be when I served crusty slices dripping with butter at their first meeting.

I had just put the breadbowl on the radiator to rise when Jim called to say there were three medical speakers and was I sure I didn't want him to take them to the club. I seemed tired—

No-o-o-o. I wasn't one bit tired. I'd love to have them.

"I'll be home early. We have to eat and run because the meeting is at eight o'clock."

I jerked a leg of lamb out of the freezer, put it in the auxiliary oven, poked down the bread, peeled some potatoes and put them on to soak, washed the lettuce, thinking all the while that I'd make a pan of hard rolls too. Wouldn't the Brownies love it when I gave each of them a doll loaf to take home?

I went upstairs to get dressed and was just putting on my lipstick when the milling herd arrived.

Mari bellowed, "Mother, where are you? They're here!"

I arrived in the kitchen to be met by a surging mass of children, giggling and slapping and pushing each other. I just had time to note that the bread was bulging over the pan and oozing toward the radiator when Phyllis, behaving as if she had never seen me before, stalked over and held out her hand. "How do you do. I'm Phyllis Bean, the President. I would like to invite you to attend our meeting." She saluted smartly, yelled, "Come on," and they thundered down the basement stairs, followed by Heidi, Dagmar and Spot. Phyllis' strident commands echoed through the house over the scuffling and stamping. *"Don't* throw your stuff around. *Hang* it up! *She* won't like it! Put your things on the table and BE QUIET!"

Just as I was dumping the bread out on the breadboard, Mari opened the basement door. "Where's the treat?"

"I've got a surprise for you. I'm going to serve hot bread and butter."

"When'll it be done?"

"Oh pretty soon."

"Mo-ther-r-r. We always have our treat right after the meeting. Haven't we got some cookies and fruit juice? We always have cookies and fruit juice. Hurry up! Phyllis is waiting."

Slightly dampened, I opened a can of pineapple juice, found some soggy graham crackers and carried them down to the gameroom to find the Brownies all lined up at the table waiting for me.

"I can't stay but a minute. I'm making bread," I began.

Phyllis interrupted me. "You may put the tray here in front of me. We're late so we won't have Opening. Meeting's called to order. SIT DOWN!"

They dropped to the benches and I sat down on the wing chair.

"We'll have roll call first so *she* can tell who you are. Angela, begin." Angela—Cherie, Colleen—Gloria—Jane—Katie, Sumiko, I tried to keep track of them, but they soon began to look as much alike as little brown buttons on a card. Snub noses, bright eyes, pink cheeks, even ours melted into the group, stared at me from under their lashes and behaved as if they'd never been in the gameroom before.

Phyllis took a small black notebook out of her pocket. "Patty? Read the secretary's report."

Patty, a tall thin child with a brown horsetail and bangs, shrugged and continued to sit with her back to the group, reading. She jumped as Phyllis snapped, "Patty, pay attention. Put that book down. Read the minutes," but she didn't turn around or stop reading.

Phyllis thrust out her chin and started to rise. "Pa-a-a-tty!"

Patty slowly closed the book and looked at the wall. "I forgot the minutes, but let's see. We had oatmeal cookies and juice and took a hike to gather skeleton leaves, and they were all sopping wet, and I don't remember what we played, but it was some dumb old game." She resumed her reading.

Madame President closed her eyes and sighed. "It was Drop the Handkerchief, and we worked on our nature notebooks. It was the meeting before when we took the hike and gathered skeleton leaves. Jane, the treasurer's report."

Jane, so eager she was pointing, got up, flicked back her braids and reeled off her litany. "We've had four meetings, we have sixteen members, four times sixteen times five cents is three dollars and five cents. Mari's been to two and Sally's been to one, that's fifteen, and now today we should have," looked up at the ceiling, "four dollars and ten cents. Everybody bring their dues?"

There were grumbles. "All you ever think about is money —you're just supposed to collect the dues, not tell us all the money we have all the time," several minor altercations, and a couple of slaps, but the funds were finally forthcoming and Jane spent the rest of the meeting (and most of the meetings thereafter) lovingly counting her nickels.

As the meeting progressed, it was indeed awe-inspiring to observe Madame President's simple technique for managing garrulous females. Rambling wordiness was stopped by "We've heard that." Personal reminiscences were quelled with "We know. Go on." All questions by committee members were dismissed with "I'll take care of it," and swift scribbles in Phyllis' little black book.

Ten minutes later Phyllis yawned, stretched widely and said, "Meeting's adjourned. Let's eat."

They swallowed the crackers and gulped the pineapple juice and Madame President turned a stern eye on me. "What have you planned for us to do today?"

I looked wildly around me trying to remember a harmless project from the Leader's Guide and dredged up something to the effect that children like best to do what their mothers do. I said, "I'm making some bread. Would you like to help me?"

My loyal offspring promptly chorused, "Mo-ther-r-r!" But Phyllis stared at me through her glasses and said, "Bread is Homemaking. The Troop may form in line."

They rushed upstairs and Heidi dropped back beside me. "That old Phyllis can't boss me. I'm going up to my room and play with Squeaky." She ducked through the mob of giggling, pushing, shoving children and disappeared.

The Brownies ranged themselves in a ring around me and were wide-eyed with admiration as I began to divide the dough into portions, flatten it, fold it over, and roll it preparatory to kneading it.

Phyllis stopped me. "You have to tell us what you're doing so we'll learn how."

"First I knead it, then I form it into loaves—"

"Why, why, what, what, where, where, who, who," it was like a nest of owlets.

Jane said, "Could we each have a piece so we could learn to knead it? You have to give us eighteen pieces—"

Grabbing a large hunk, I floured the kitchen table, divided the dough and distributed it.

As I watched them joyously slapping the dough and each other, roaring and giggling and exchanging jokes, "What's the news, Booze"—"Where's your dough, Bo," I was of two minds. It was torment to watch my nice white dough turn into slippery gray erasers, but it was also touching to watch them chew their tongues, crinkle their brows, and bite their lips in their earnest efforts to imitate my motions.

Phyllis made no attempt to knead. Instead she stalked around after me, quoting tirelessly from her Brownie Handbook. "Be sure the handles of the pots and pans are turned so they will not be over the edge of the stove." Her glasses winked disapprovingly at me as she turned the handle of the melted butter pan toward the back of the stove. "Brownies avoid needless accidents by being careful."

"You missed the boat, Goat"—"You hit the table, Mable"—"You give me a pain, Jane"—screams of insane laughter.

Reeling from the noise and confusion, I was tempted to tell Phyllis that intelligent women avoid Brownies and one with an ounce of gray matter wouldn't make bread.

At first they were content to work at the table, then as elbows bumped and dough stuck to hands, they moved to the shelves under the windows, the working surfaces under the cupboards, even on to the drainboards by the sink, trailing flour behind them.

I turned my back for a moment and a breadball whizzed by my ear, followed by a fusillade of breadballs. I banged my spoon down on the stove and was filling my lungs for a bellow of rage when Phyllis beat me to it.

"STOP THAT!" They froze. In a long-suffering voice she added, "*She's* trying to be a Leader. Now KNEAD!"

She reached up and got a saucer from the cupboard, put my spoon on it, wiped a minuscule spat of butter from the top of the stove and said, "When you are cooking, put the spoon you use in a saucer so you won't get your stove messy."

Meanwhile the Brownies were watching me covertly to see how much they could get away with. When I did nothing but obey Phyllis, they returned to kneading what were by this time greasy little black balls.

Phyllis jerked my arm. "Don't you use a recipe?"

A little grimly I said that I'd made bread so many times I no longer had to use a recipe. She clucked, "Haven't you got a cook book? Could I see the recipe? Brownies always follow a recipe. In that way they do not waste good food."

It was clear from the way my feet stuck to the floor that even a Brownie occasionally wasted a grain or so, but I counted to ten and chose the cookbook which worked laboriously from stalk to stomach, describing each process in wordy, unnecessary detail, and handed it to Phyllis. "Here. Read it aloud. Every word of it."

Phyllis took a deep breath and began: "'In the old days women. Made yeast at home us.' Oh yes, 'Usually from hops or, as.'" It made no sense at all, but the Brownies seemed to enjoy it and I got a chance to put the bread in the pans to rise.

"How are we going to bake *our* loaves?" they chorused.

I produced a large muffin pan and a pastry brush, and they took turns greasing the sections (and their stomachs) and placed their revolting blobs therein.

"Now put them in the oven to cook while we clean up," Phyllis ordered.

"But bread has to rise—" I began.

They chorused, "We don't care. We haven't got time. We want to eat it. Put it in the oven—"

Clouds of flour filled the air along with the Brownie work song, "We have tidied everything, everything, everything, we have tidied everything, we are Brownies," to the tune of London Bridge.

The fact that they even attempted to clean up after themselves softened me somewhat, and I turned to jelly as I heard from all sides, "Gee, you Jay kids sure are lucky"—"I wish my mother knew how to make bread"—"Boy, I wish *she* was our Leader. We never get to cook."

I heard, "Daddy's kitchen sure is messy—" and turned to find Heidi standing in the doorway flanked on either side by Dagmar and Spot.

Phyllis said, "Take those dogs out of here. Animals are unsanitary in a kitchen."

"They are not. Anyway, I notice you don't do any work." Heidi stuck out her tongue at Phyllis and left.

I too had noticed that while the Brownies were sweeping and scrubbing the drainboards and covering the working surfaces with streaks of paste, their President sat on the window seat swinging her fat legs, her glasses ranging back and forth, back and forth, picking out flaws in their efforts. But I said, "I'm sorry Heidi seemed rude—"

In a detached voice, Phyllis said, "She was rude, but it's because she's jealous. She'll be polite when she gets to be a Brownie. We're always polite." She stared at me through her glasses. "This was a good meeting considering it's your first. Of course you went and made the dough before we got here, but that's because you didn't know any better. Next time we'll make it, with a recipe. Brownies do everything for themselves."

She slid off the window seat, opened the oven door and took out the muffin pan. "All done. Everybody take one."

They weren't done, they were streaky, gray, poisonous looking puffballs. I said hastily, "Wouldn't you like to have me bake the rolls? You could each have one of those—"

"No thanks. We like our own best." They devoured their puffballs with great relish.

Phyllis looked at the clock. "Get your coats on. We'll make our Goodnight Tunnel up here so *she* can see it. HURRY UP!" She turned to me. "We're late, so you'll have to drive home the ones who live far away."

They galumphed down the basement stairs again and I put the bread in the oven, hoping it would get done before dinner and wondering dazedly if I was strong enough to stand a series of Monday afternoons.

The Brownies came back upstairs and formed two lines, making arches with their arms. Singing, "Night is come, owls are out, beetles hum round about," the two at the end ducked under and two by two, the Tunnel diminished, leaving me six to drive home.

I was just cramming them into the station wagon when Jim drove up with three doctors in the car! Dinner guests! I'd completely forgotten them.

Calling to Jim that I'd be right back, I delivered the

Brownies who seemed to live as far away as possible, dashed into Murphy's and grabbed frozen vegetables and a lemon pie and panted back into the house at two minutes to six.

Mari put her hands on her hips. "It's a good thing we're Brownies. I put the potatoes on and finished cleaning up the kitchen, and Sally made the salad and Heidi set the table." Her back even looked like mine as she slammed around muttering, "I wonder if anything I say to you has the least effect."

Jim came out to the kitchen just as I was taking two small loaves of bread out of the oven. "Is this all there is? Umm-m-m, this house smells delicious and you do too." He hugged me. "You have flour on your nose. We've been sitting in there smelling fresh bread and suffering." Cutting one loaf into six slices and buttering it, he said, "By the way, how did Phyllis like your first meeting?"

Before I had a chance to describe the bedlam, Mari said, "Oh Daddy, we had the neatest time! Phyllis showed Mother how to make bread with a recipe. Mother was just neat, Daddy, really she was."

4

I'M HUMAN TOO

OCTOBER was erratic, brilliant sunshine one day, cold and dreary the next, but not half as unpredictable as my emotional barometer which rose and fell without warning.

The first coolness developed when I discovered that Monday was not the only day on which to expect visits from my newfound friends. The girls trailed home, bringing strings of Brownies actual and potential, and Phyllis announced that she would spend every afternoon at our house turning me into a Leader.

"Won't your mother need you?" I asked hopefully.

Phyllis shook her head. "Mymother doesn't get home until after five. Those dumb secretaries would get everything all balled up if she did."

"Does your mother work?" I asked.

"No, but she's president of just about everything in town. Are you making a pie? What kind? Mymother buys them frozen. Do you make cookies? Why? Mymother uses a mix—"

I served gallons of cambric tea and hundreds of cookies

54

and wound in and out and around Brownies trying to cook dinner and discovered quite a number of things not included in the Leader's Guide.

"Do you visit the juvenile court? Why not? Mymother says there are no delinquent children, only delinquent parents. Why?"

I looked at Phyllis, controlled the urge to reply and shook my head.

"Mymother says it is the duty of every mother to visit the city council once a week. Do you visit the city council once a week? Why not?"

I shook my head.

I also shook my head at parks, jails, water and light departments, historical societies, art museums, day nurseries, bird sanctuaries, Council of Churches and labor union meetings, all requiring the untiring supervision of "Mymother."

"Gee!" Phyllis asked, "what do you do all day?"

By the time Jim came home I had had so much help and so many suggestions that I had a tendency to swish around muttering that my initial mistake was in getting engaged, to which he replied that it was *my* idea to add all these additional "why'ers" when I already had three of my own.

On the following Monday when Mrs. Burton came in with the Brownies, I saw that she not only was pregnant, she looked as if she might have her baby at the meeting. She was a ship in full sail, and her wide brown eyes were shadowed by that patient, bovine expression worn in the last stages.

While the Brownies roared, "Hi, Mrs. Jay" and clattered down the basement stairs, Mrs. Burton sat down and pressed her palms against her temples. "I'll just rest a minute if you don't mind, I get so out of breath—"

I was so out of breath at the possibility of being THE Leader before the afternoon was over that I barely took in her gentle apologies. She was so sorry to leave me alone at the first meeting, she didn't get out of the doctor's office until after five, she tried to call me but the line was busy—

"MRS. BUR-R-R-R-R-TON?" came from the foot of the stairs.

She stood up, holding on to the edge of the table to get her balance. "My, the girls had such a wonderful time making bread. I didn't know anyone ever made bread any more. They all called me up and told me it was the best meeting—"

Instantly I was warm with the glow of appreciated effort and could hardly wait to hear Patty's flattering report of all the fun they'd had.

We entered the gameroom just as Phyllis snapped, "Patty? Secretary's report."

With her eyes still glued to her book, Patty mumbled, "We made bread."

Slightly dashed, I told Mrs. Burton I had the treat all ready, fresh chocolate chip cookies and lemonade.

She shook her head. "We don't provide the treat. The children take turns bringing it. The Troop furnishes the treat and all equipment. It encourages group participation and consideration of others. I do hope Phyllis will let us take a walk, it's such a lovely day."

While she was talking, Phyllis was whipping through the meeting in her customary abrupt fashion and I found myself wondering if a little less laissez-faire on the part of Mrs. Burton would produce less dictatorship in Phyllis.

Phyllis said, "O.K. Let's eat." One of them dug in a capacious brown bag and produced a large can of grapefruit juice and a box of cookies which was greeted with, "Peeyew! Bitter old grapefruit, I hate grapefruit. Storebought cookies! I hate storebought," but nonetheless they were gulped down.

Phyllis came over and stood in front of us. "Let's take a hike in honor of Mrs. Jay's being new. We can show you all sorts of things I'll bet you've never seen. Nature and all that stuff." She turned to the scrabbling, giggling group and screamed, "We're going to take a hike. Get your coats on. Don't forget your galoshes. Hurry up. BE QUIET!" at which they all nodded submissively and began to put on their coats.

Mrs. Burton led the Troop and I brought up the rear. The pale sun shone on soft green fir tips, diamond droplets hung from glossy, dark green shrubs, chrysanthemums blazed from each garden, their spicy fragrance blending with the heady scent of cedar and salt water.

I watched the Brownies hop up on walls and teeter along with outstretched arms, indulge in foolish puppy chases, stoop suddenly to examine a leaf and then swoop off to hang from a branch and drop with a crow of delight.

Picking a spicy tip of fir and holding it to my nose, I could see my father striding along in front of me in the Montana forests, I could feel the pine needles slithering under foot, and could hear Mother's, "Darsie! Mary's only eight. She can't walk along that slippery log—" and Daddy's, "Sure she can. Children have prehensile toes. Come on Mary—" and my skin tingled with the memory of walking over the river and meeting Daddy's outstretched hand.

Mari dropped back beside me. "Look, Mother!" A mother cat gingerly stepped across a roof, a kitten dangling from her mouth. "Aren't they smart? They just take a teeny pinch of skin. Did you ever notice how Gloria bounces when she walks, like she was stuffed with balloons or something? Look! This poor old tree is trying to lift up the sidewalk so its roots can stretch. I'll bet trees hate being squashed under sidewalks—"

Then Phyllis' coxswain's bellow to her Troop, "Hey! Watchit. There's a truck coming. Aw, that is not a pine, it's a Douglas fir. Hey, everybody. Lookit that red tree. Can I break off a branch and take it home, Mrs. Burton? Mymother knows every kind of tree there is. She's on the Arboretum Board."

Mari clutched my hand. "Do you like being a Leader, Mother? I'll tell you about the Brownies. That one with the pretty, sad kind of face is Minnie. Her mother works nights and she does all the housework and helps with her brother's paper route. She's teacher's pet and no wonder. Boy, is she ever smart!

"That one who walks with her toes turned out, kind of like a duck, that's Katie. She's German, and Cherie's French. She's that little dark one who looks about six but is really nine. Do you know what? Their mothers can't even speak English! That's why they talk kind of funny sometimes and they write funny too, but boy oh boy are they good in geography!

"That fat one's Gloria, the bouncy one. Her mother owns the bakery up at the corner and boy does she eat! Phyllis told her if she'd quit eating, she wouldn't be such a blimp. But not Gloria. Bread, cake, candy, always stuffing her mouth. Why she even brings stuff to school and hides it in her desk. Regular chipmunk and is she ever dumb!

"Patty's the one who reads all the time. Does she ever forget stuff! Phyllis says she'd forget her head if it wasn't screwed on. She's the tallest girl in our room, and she pretends she doesn't care, walks with her knees bent. Phyllis calls her Shorty and Stringbean so she won't mind being tall, but it doesn't do any good with old Patty—

"And, Mother, do you know what? Sumiko can just take old dead branches and make the prettiest things! She says her mother teaches ladies how to make flower arrangements."

It poured on and on. Not only was I getting a good thumbnail sketch of each Brownie, but I was hearing more about school than I'd heard since Mari started to kindergarten.

I was grateful for the opportunity of entertaining any and all Brownies if it meant the uncorking of our reserved elder daughter.

This gratitude lasted two days. Then Emily, our beloved and reliable baby sitter, dropped by after school to borrow a book. Emily was seventeen, a senior in high school and so luscious her dates screamed by the house night and day in their jalopies courting Emily and striking terror to my heart for fear they would come screeching around the corner and hit a Brownie.

Emily sat down at the kitchen table with the children and said, "Say, Mrs. Jay, I hear you're going to be a Leader. You'll be great, you're so easy going. I've been a Scout for years and years." She beamed around the table. "I can even build a fire by rubbing two Boy Scouts together."

Mari and Sally and Durdey and Patty and Gloria and Heidi doubled up with worshipful laughter and resumed their envious stares at Emily's long blonde locks and fuchsia lipstick and nailpolish.

Phyllis stared at Emily and then sniffed, "I've heard that joke before."

Emily saluted. "Maybe, but a Girl Scout is courteous."

A faint flush tinged Phyllis' cheeks as she returned the salute. "I'm sorry, Emily."

Jimmy, Murphy's delivery boy, banged open the kitchen door and, seeing Emily, stood clutching the box of groceries to his bosom. "Hi, Gorgeous, how come you're here?"

Emily batted her eyelashes at Jimmy and a quart of milk dropped to the floor. "Jimmy here can tell you I'm a good Scout. He used to drive me over to Camp last summer when I was a Program Aide. Didn't you, Man?"

Man gazed helplessly at her and mumbled, "You can say that again."

Emily turned back to the children who were watching with openmouthed absorption. "You girls may not know it, but Jimmy here is an Eagle Scout and believe you me, that takes some doing."

Jimmy swelled, dumped the groceries in the general direction of the kitchen table, sat down and began to regale us with harrowing exploits. I'd known Jimmy since he was ten and was aware that he lived a vivid imaginary existence, but I'd also found there was usually a springboard of fact from which he dove off into space. He had hung by a frayed rope on the face of a five hundred foot cliff. His Leader, with the rest of his Troop, hadn't found him until late the next day. "Yay man, that climb was sure tough!" (That episode was in the paper.) He had hung by his hands from a railroad trestle while the train thundered overhead. "We sure looked like a bunch of monkeys hanging there. Our Leader was so scared he almost had a heart attack." (Jimmy's father had almost had apoplexy when he heard the original version.) He had been lost for two days in the Olympic mountains. "Some dumb guy tried to cross that range with only a bow and arrow. They never even found his skeleton!" said Jimmy with great relish.

Emily leaned her chin on her hand and looked into his eyes and breathed, "Boy! I'll bet you're strong!"

The children gulped and breathed, "Gosh!" Jimmy flexed his muscles and allowed each one to feel them, while I gazed at the back of his heartbreakingly thin young neck and thought of his Leader. I could have kissed Emily when she finally jeered, "Yep, you're a tiger all right. Now go on about your business. I've got to help Mrs. Jay."

While I browned the meat for the stew, Emily peeled the vegetables and told me leadership was a breeze, just a breeze. Kids liked anything as long as they knew you liked them. Some Leaders tried to make it hard like school. Handbook Happy. Others pushed the panic button all the time and kept saying "don't." Like that Miss Dale. "Don'ty Dale" they called her, because she was always and forever saying

"Don't." Like that time she took Emily's Troop to the Zoo when they were Brownies, to see the different kinds of bears —why, that kid who got her head stuck in the bear's cage would never have even thought of it if Don'ty Dale hadn't kept saying, "Don't climb on the railings. Scouts don't climb on railings."

I wondered what Miss Dale was supposed to say, while the children shrieked with laughter and begged for more tales of Don'ty Dale.

"Don'ty visited Camp last year to give us nature talks. The talks were neat, really they were, and boy can she ever spot birds, but she kept saying, 'Don't do this' and 'Don't do that,' so-o-o-o, the kids shortsheeted her bed."

Mari was watching me to see how I was taking all this. She said unsurely, "Mother wouldn't be like that, would you, Mother?"

I hastily asked Emily what Miss Dale did when they short-sheeted her bed.

Emily shrugged, "Oh, she just laughed. She's a good Scout."

These tales encouraged our Brownie guests to take turns recounting several hair-raisers which had happened to Mrs. Burton's Troop. Patty had disappeared when they were at the parade, and they finally had to go home without her. Guess what! She'd gone to a movie! Gloria didn't go straight home from a meeting and a policeman had to bring her home in a prowler car! Boy, was her mother mad! Minnie had poked a wasps' nest, and Mrs. Burton had to rub mud on her. Did Minnie ever swell and yell! It sure was fun to be a Brownie!

Emily winked at me. "Don't believe everything you hear." She pointed to a row of carrots, potatoes and onions and chanted, "All you have to do, is toss 'em in the stew." She looked up at the kitchen clock. "I've got to scram. Old

Snake Eyes wants us to write a theme on myths for gosh sakes. Do you know anything about myths, Mrs. Jay?"

I said not much but we had a book on mythology and what kind of myths did Old Snake Eyes prefer?

"Oh, Greek or Norse. Anything. She's nuts for myths." She threw an arm casually around my shoulder. "If we could cool an A on myths, I might just get a B in English."

I was still helping Emily cool an A on myths when Jim came in saying he had to eat right away, as he had a lot of house calls to make.

Emily said, "I'll write this tonight and bring it over so you can read it and see if it's O.K. Thanks, ever so much." She offered to walk Phyllis and Durdey and Patty and Gloria part way home, told our girls to hurry up and set the table, and sauntered out the back door, saying, "See you tomorrow. 'Bye now."

Jim said did I realize it was six o'clock and why wasn't dinner ready. By biting my lips I just managed to keep still, but Sally said, "Remember, Daddy, you said, 'In our family it's all or nothing.'"

We spent the following week end cleaning the basement, which is quite a project, as there is a furnace room, a wood room, a laundry room, a bathroom, two halls, a fruit room, two large storage rooms, a central area called "the middle room," the tool room, and the gameroom. I kept following Jim around saying, "What'll I do if a Brownie gets hurt, or lost, or run over, or bitten by a dog?" until he finally said, "Now look here, I told you before you got into this that our Scout Leader was a Superman. As a matter of fact nothing ever happened in our Troop that was in the least dramatic. One boy broke his leg, but that was his own fault. Now suppose you concentrate on helping me sort all this stuff and stop brooding about things that probably never will happen."

On the last Monday of October, the Brownies arrived

laden with bags and bundles and bursting with self-importance. Mrs. Burton was carrying a small blue mirror. She said, "Perhaps I'd better warn you that we have a thrilling surprise for you."

As we entered the gameroom, Phyllis ordered the Brownies to line up for inspection. Tall, short, fat, thin, blonde, dark, Oriental, Occidental, now they not only did not look alike to me, their only common denominator seemed to be large gravestone teeth.

Phyllis stalked back and forth in front of them. "Fasten your belt, Patty; pull up your socks, Gloria; tie your shoe, Sally; straighten your cap, Minnie—" Each head was capped with a little brown beanie, each Brownie dress was crisp and neat, hands and faces were clean and eyes shone with expectancy. Phyllis snapped, "Committees get to work."

There was an immediate scrabble for the bags out of which came a green paper tablecloth, paper napkins, paper plates, candles and what appeared to be costumes.

Mrs. Burton stood up and took off her coat. She had disguised her protuberance with a frilly green apron. She smiled apologetically. "I still can't decide whether the apron accents or discounts my interesting condition, but I can't button my uniform, and I promised Phyllis I'd wear it."

Heidi's eyes were glued to Mrs. Burton's stomach. "Are you preg—" she began, and I hastily asked what the surprise was.

Mrs. Burton said that Brownies were supposed to attend four meetings before they were Invested, this was the fourth meeting and just in the nick of time too as far as she was concerned. "Pat Smith, she's our District Director, you know, hoped to get here in time for the Investiture—" She said something else, but due to a loud altercation among the bustling committee, I missed it.

Phyllis placed the blue mirror on the floor in front of the fireplace, came over to me and said, "Could you help us cut some forest branches? Mrs. Burton can't reach up any more."

Heidi nodded. "I thought so."

Phyllis gave her a withering look. "We have to make a forest with a little pool."

So Heidi and I and the decoration committee went out to the ravine north of the house and hacked off some branches of fir and cedar and staggered back with armloads of sopping wet evergreens to find Pat Smith talking to Mrs. Burton.

Pat grinned at me. "I told you I couldn't resist a Scout ceremony. Just wait until you see this." She went on talking to Mrs. Burton while I tried to help the decoration committee arrange the branches around the mirror to give the effect of a little forest pool. They would have none of it, told me I didn't know how, and stacked boughs like cordwood until they had achieved a small corral with an opening at one end.

Phyllis inspected it, rearranged a couple of branches, and then snapped, "O.K. everybody. Katie? We're ready."

The Brownies dropped to the floor in a semi-circle in front of a battered screen rescued from the Goodwill pile.

The screen wavered dangerously, due to a muffled fight going on behind it, and Katie, the stolid blonde German child, appeared and saluted. "I'm Katie. I'm the announcer. This is the Brownie Story. It was written by Mrs. Juliana Horatia Ewing in the olden days. We have fixed it like TV. It's about Mary and Tommy who wouldn't help their grandmother and father who was a tailor. They were lazy and cranky until they saw the Wise Old Owl who turned them into Brownies. That's how we got started." She retired behind the screen, donned an apron and reappeared as the crabby grandmother.

As the play progressed, my sympathies were with Mary and Tommy who were pretty good sports considering their background. Grandmother told about the little people, the father merely sat crosslegged and sniveled, "Bairns are a burden" while ripping up a dishtowel, and the Wise Old Owl, unmistakably Phyllis in a brown crepe paper cocoon, snapped, "Stop being so lazy. Whyn't you act like the little people and do some work around here?"

In the next act the "little people," four loathsomely smug Brownies, appeared and bustled around cleaning and making disparaging remarks about "that lazy old Mary and Tommy."

Act three was in the forest. The Wise Old Owl croaked, "Whyn't you look in the water?" They looked, discovered themselves, there was a miraculous transformation, and Mary and Tommy took up the frenzied sweeping and the disparaging remarks.

Katie said, "The End" and the cast came back and bowed and led the clapping.

Mrs. Burton murmured, "The more I watch, the more I find it difficult to feel bereft because the 'little people' are no longer with us."

Phyllis then ordered Mari and Sally upstairs to put on their new uniforms, told me to take Heidi and go upstairs too, and wait until she called us, adding that she supposed Heidi would have to come to their Investiture although she really shouldn't be there.

Heidi began to growl and it took me the entire fifteen minute wait to dissuade her from sicking Spot and Dagmar on "that bossy old Phyllis."

The scene that greeted us when we returned made my heart come up in my throat. A circle of Brownies singing softly, candles grasped in fat little hands casting flickering shadows on bright pink cheeks and shining eyes, pride radiating from them like sunshine.

Mrs. Burton beckoned to Mari and Sally. They walked over and stood looking up at her. She said, "Do you want to be Brownies?" Smiling like a Madonna, she looked tenderly down into their serious upturned faces and asked each one, "Are you ready to promise to do your best to love God and your country and to help other people, especially those at home?"

They gulped and nodded and she affixed small gold pins to their collars and led them to the opening of the corral.

"*When* can I be a Brownie, Mother?" Heidi whispered.

"As soon as you are in the second grade—" I whispered back.

My eyes swam as Mari and Sally solemnly turned one another around saying, "Twist me and turn me and show me the elf, I look in the water and see—myself!"

Phyllis stepped forward, her expression as angelic as a choir girl. "Welcome to Troop Fifty." She handed each of them a lighted candle, they joined the circle and began to sing, "Now the day is over—"

It was almost too much for me. How could I have any doubts? Just as I was about to melt down into a pool of sentimental tears toward any and all children, Phyllis snapped on the overhead lights. "Gloria! Get the cake."

Gloria, the stoutest Brownie of them all, waddled importantly out of the room and came back bearing an enormous cake with eighteen candles and two Leader candles in the middle. She put it down on the table, put her arms around it saying, "I guess my mother made this so I get to blow out the candles," puffed her cheeks into twin balloons and blew. Instantly an explosion of noise filled the room.

"That's not fair, that's our Troop birthday cake—we're all supposed to blow," which Pat Smith silenced by holding up three fingers.

"How did you do that?" I marveled.

"It's the silence sign. We use it whenever we want to get attention." She walked over to the cake. "How would you like to have me divide this for you?"

The cake was cut, divided and devoured in less time than it takes to tell it, and joy reigned unconfined.

Mari skidded to a stop in front of me. "Mother! Wasn't that the neatest play, and isn't this the neatest party you've ever been to?"

Sally stopped tearing around long enough to say prayerfully, "Mother! I just can't believe it. I'm a real Brownie!" To which Heidi replied bitterly, "Yeah, and I notice I got the littlest piece of cake."

It was such a neat party and there was so much screaming and racing around that I finally put my fingers in my ears and was astonished to see Mrs. Burton and Pat Smith sitting right in the middle of it and carrying on a conversation as casually as if they were on a secluded park bench.

Pat Smith pointed toward her chest and then toward the door. "I've got to get back."

As we stood at the front door, she grinned and pulled her hat forward at a jaunty angle. "Ready or not, you shall be caught. Mrs. Burton isn't going to last much longer and you know it. Come on down and register."

5

THE VOICE OF EXPERIENCE

$\mathcal{S}$TILL bemused by the charm of the Investiture, I announced at breakfast the next morning that I was going downtown right after lunch to register as Leader so I'd be ready to take over Mrs. Burton's Troop when she had her baby.

Jim shook his head. Was I sure I knew what I was doing? If he knew me, I'd get in so deep, my example would discourage every other mother from ever becoming a Leader. Wouldn't it be just as well to wait until I'd looked into this Scouting business a little further?

Why wait? This was one activity about which I had no qualms whatsoever.

The girls said nothing but looked at one another from under their lashes, a sure sign that I've said or done some Mo-ther-r-r-y thing.

Mari began, "We don't want to hurt your feelings, Mommy, but we'd rather have a real Leader, not our Mother."

Sally added, "Mrs. Burton hasn't any children, so she's never crabby, but you're used to children—"

Heidi delivered the final blow. "Looks to me like Phyllis is the Leader anyway."

They clattered off to school, and in the quiet of the house the reaction set in. Would I be a good Leader? Did I actually have time for this activity? Would our children get the full benefit of a Brownie Troop if it was held in their own home and led by their mother?

By the time I got down to the Council, I was thoroughly whipped. It was a little cheering to be greeted like an old family friend by the brisk assistants but disturbing to be told that Pat Smith was out but Miss Dale, the assistant Executive Director, could see me in just a minute.

Don'ty Dale! Wouldn't you know! Before I got a chance to adjust to this blow, I was ushered into an inner office and introduced to a woman with the commanding presence (and unfortunate memory pattern) of my first grade-school principal. I fully expected her to say, "Mary? What have you been up to now?"

Miss Dale stood tall and erect in her green uniform. Her aquiline features were expressionless as she regarded me with piercing light gray eyes. "Mrs. Jay? Sit down please."

Even the same voice. Authoritative, detached, deep.

Automatically I sat down, folded my hands and awaited my punishment.

She pulled various forms toward her while I tried to think up some plausible excuse as to why I had dared to enter the principal's office.

"First shall we take your qualifications as a Scout Leader? Were you a Girl Scout?" No. A teacher? No. A nurse? No. Interested in athletics? Heavens no! As nothing I had ever done, with the possible exception of having girl children, fitted in with what I assumed to be her conception of Leader material, I offered illogically that my husband was a doctor.

She frowned slightly, wrote physician's wife on the various forms and then leaned back in her chair. Did I believe in the Girl Scout Promise and Laws and in the democratic principles that guide the organization? Yes. Did I have a liking for all children? I thought of Phyllis Bean and said, well—some more than others. Was I willing to take time, to take training, to cooperate? Yes. Did I feel that I had the ability to guide girls and to get along with people? So far the girls had been guiding me, but we seemed to be getting along all right. Was I in possession of good health, good sense and the highest of moral principles? I nodded, skirting the good sense and knowing exactly why that Brownie had stuck her head into the railing around the bear's cage.

Her pale gray eyes regarded me speculatively. "What do you think of our program so far?"

Marvelous, fascinating, Leader's Guide was an inspired document—I knew I was burbling but couldn't help myself. Of course I'd had a few difficulties—

Without warning, Miss Dale gave a sharp cry of laughter, "Difficulties! When I became a Leader, I didn't even know that eagles court in mid-air!"

And for the rest of that conference I saw Miss Dale soaring through the treetops in search of a mate!

I'd endured what seemed to me hours of relentless investigation when Miss Dale abruptly stood up and held out her hand. "Thank you for coming in, Mrs. Jay. Do not hesitate to call on us if you feel you need help." She crunched my fingers in a grip of iron and dismissed me.

I crept out of the principal's office, all my ancient dislike of that lady boiling over on Miss Dale's head. How dare that relentless bird of prey tell me how to take care of children? Was she married? Did she have any children? Had she any conception of the quicksilver emotions of small girls? How maddening, endearing, fascinating, infuriating and unpredictable they could be in the space of one hour, even when they were your own flesh and blood and you loved them to distraction? No wonder she had so much trouble getting Leaders. She spoke of Brownies as if they were age-limited units—

By the time I stopped at Murphy's I was breathing fire.

Susan Blake was standing in front of the vegetable section eyeing the display as if it were a collection of shrunken heads. She picked up a stalk of broccoli and shuddered. "I loathe vegetables. Have to eat them as a good example for Peggy. Be thankful you have three, they're so busy fighting they don't notice what you eat. Say, Phyllis tells me that you are going to take over Mrs. Burton's Troop when she produces. Who's going to be your assistant, or haven't you chosen her yet?"

I described the grilling I had just endured and added that it was much easier to become a Judge of the Supreme Court than it was to qualify as a Scout Leader and no wonder they had trouble getting Leaders.

Susan watched me with amused eyes while I ranted. Was Miss Dale trying to run a house and be a wife and mother *and* a Brownie Leader? Oh no! *She* sat loftily in the Council quoting impossible rules and regulations while the Leaders did all the work. Did they or did they not want Leaders? And another thing—

"Calm down or you'll explode." Susan fanned me with the broccoli. "Sorry to disappoint you, Chum, but to me, you sound just like a mother. I've told you I used to be a playground instructor. Believe me, you have no idea how deathly sick you can get of all the dear little children and their eager interfering mothers, each of whom knows more about your job than you do. What did she say that made you so mad?"

Well, she didn't actually *say* anything, it was just her attitude. After all, I was just planning to be a Leader, not a kidnaper. I supposed they did have to be careful but—

"Now you're talking," Susan said. "What about Mrs. Burton?"

Well, heaven knew I was more than grateful to her for taking our girls into her Troop, and she *was* pregnant, and she had been a Leader for two years and probably was sick and tired of it, but she just sat there, looking pretty, while Phyllis Bean ran the Troop. I didn't mean to sound critical, but she seemed so limp and unenthusiastic—

Susan shook her head. "Mothers! You'll have your moments of unenthusiasm, believe me. What I was going to ask you before you took off was, how would you like me for your assistant?"

"Susan! How heavenly—"

"Now take it easy. I'm ready to use fair means or foul to get Peggy to stop following me around and whining 'Why can't I be a Brownie?' Therefore, I hereby make you a proposition. I'll be your assistant and play games until they drop dead of exhaustion, IF you will promise that I never have to talk to a mother. Is it a deal?"

It not only was a deal, it was the first bright spot in an otherwise murky horizon. "Heaven only knows how Miss Dale will react. She has a positive mania for the number sixteen."

Susan waved that away. "I'll handle Miss Dale. Don't forget, I was a Girl Scout in my youth. Come on, let's go across the street to Bessie's and toast our probable demise in a cup of coffee."

Bessie greeted us fondly and plopped down huge mugs of coffee. "Phyllis Bean tells me you're the new Brownie Leader, Mrs. Jay." She swiped at the table with a gray rag, "You'll need something stronger than coffee to handle that young one."

Susan leaned her chin on her hand and grinned across the table at me. "Aside from Phyllis, with whom I'm well acquainted, what seems to be your main problem?"

The waiting list. Mothers called night and day begging to have little Sandra or Darleen or Myrnajean in the Troop.

"For the time being we will ignore it. I've checked and there are one hundred and fifty potential Brownies in our school alone. Obviously they cannot all be jammed into one Troop. Next?"

Mrs. Burton already had a full Troop and with Mari and Sally and Peggy, we'd have nineteen although several of the girls were supposed to be moving away.

Again Susan waved her hand. "So what! I used to have fifty or sixty on the playground at once and I had no trouble. What am I saying? It was pure bedlam but no worse than when I had fifteen or twenty——"

"But, Susan, it says in the Leader's Guide that learning to work together and to get along with one another in a small group is the sound foundation of all Scouting and has been from the beginning and—"

Susan interrupted, "The only time I had any real trouble was when a mother appeared to insist that I wasn't being fair to little Poobah. I finally turned my playful band into a hardened bunch of guerrillas who attacked at the sight of a mother and by the end of the year we never even saw one. Seriously though, we won't have one bit of trouble if we keep mothers out of it, and I assure you the Council will fawn on us if we fill out their forms, follow their program and above all, let them alone. They are understaffed and overworked and by and large, pretty good Scouts."

"Susan, are you sure you wouldn't like to be the Leader?" I asked.

"Oh no. My main object in doing this is to shove Peggy out from under my wing. She's so mother-dominated that her teachers complain about it." She grinned companionably. "Look, we've known one another for years, we like each other and we like children. For us, it will be a cinch." She held up her mug in a toast, her hazel eyes twinkling over the rim. "To the kiddies, bless 'em, and may our strength hold up."

We clinked mugs. "And may Mrs. Burton hold out until we get indoctrinated into the ways of Leadership," I said fervently.

We parted on the giddy note that we'd invite Mrs. Burton to have a peanut butter sandwich with us on Monday and go over the Troop records.

Again I opened our front door to be greeted by shrieks of joy. Guess what! Mr. Burton had called and Mrs. Burton had an eight pound baby boy!

6

NEW BROOMS

*M*R. BURTON brought over the Troop records and Susan and I spent Wednesday and Thursday from ten in the morning until three in the afternoon going over them.

"I can't say that I agree with all of Mrs. Burton's methods," Susan mused, "but she certainly has kept accurate records, a brief account of each meeting, individual records on each girl, dues, attendance, finance—" She flipped over a list of names. "Troop Committee. We'll let them strictly alone."

"But it says in the Leader's Guide—"

"I don't care what it says in the Leader's Guide. Mothers are mothers. They'll criticize every move we make and drive us crazy with suggestions."

I was reading over the list. "But Susan, I've met most of these women up at Murphy's. I don't know them well, of course, but they seem friendly—"

"They are, but just wait until you come between them and their little darlings. Then watch them turn into tigers."

"But it says in the Leader's Guide that we should write letters to their parents enclosing questionnaires and telling them what we propose to do and warning them about the dues, the treat, and what time to come and get their children, oh yes, and when we have the Mothers' Meetings."

Susan said, "Write all the letters you want to, but no mothers' meetings. I know. Remember, I'm a teacher. Besides, nearly every mother on this list works, and the last thing she wants to do after dinner is to go to a meeting. *You* don't, do you?"

I shook my head. "No, but after all *we're* mothers too."

"Sure we're mothers, but we also have sense enough to stay away from meetings whenever it's humanly possible. They'll call you, don't worry."

I promised to write the letters and enclose the questionnaires and have them in the mail by Tuesday night.

"Don't be hurt when you don't get any answers," Susan warned bitterly. "If I had a dollar for all the unanswered notes I'd sent to mothers, I'd be a rich woman right now. Come on, let's see which one of us likes to do what best."

We checked our personal aptitudes against the table of contents in the Leader's Guide. "When I was teaching, I found that if you are uneasy and unsure with children, they sense it immediately and begin a methodical form of torture known as 'getting her goat.' My goat was gotten long ago, so I'll take care of games, arts and crafts, and Troop records. All teachers are used to filling out forms," Susan said.

I knew my weaknesses—forms, crafts and games. I thoroughly enjoyed cooking, gardening, animals, literature and dramatics and, because I had three "what'll I do-ers," felt capable of occasional snipeflights of imagination. "It's probably just as well that Mrs. Burton isn't able to break us in. We'd feel fettered and it'll be so much more fun to try out our own ideas and form our own impressions of each individual child."

Susan looked up. "What about this training program for Leaders?"

Miss Dale had said the first session was almost over and didn't begin again until February. We didn't need training, we both had children—

"Maybe it's the dregs of the teacher in me, but I think we really ought to be trained—"

I brushed that away. If we still felt we needed training by February, we'd go then. In the meantime we'd follow the Leader's Guide. "Come on, let's go down and see what you think of the gameroom."

We decided that the gameroom, which is under the living room and also is fifteen by forty-eight feet, needed a coat of paint, bright yellow to give the illusion of sunshine in the dark, dreary winter months. Susan offered to make gay curtains for the windows and let the Brownies decorate them.

"Do you suppose we could possibly get it done this week end before our first meeting?" Susan asked. "It would be wonderful to start off with a bang. Charlie would love to help—"

Jim would too although he was not what I'd call handy around the house; doctors never were—however, he did have a grateful patient—

"Good!" Susan looked at her watch. "Heavens! It's three o'clock. I've got to go so I'll be home when Peggy gets there. She's perfectly capable of taking care of herself, but I don't think so. Call me after you've talked to Jim and I'll get Charlie worked up."

At three-thirty, the children came boiling in from school with Phyllis and, bursting with enthusiasm, I sat right down and explained our dandy week-end project, finishing with, "and you can all help."

"But, Mother, Saturday's Hallowe'en!"

I knew that but we'd Trick and Treat *and* paint the gameroom.

We were in the midst of a clamorous discussion as to who

would get to paint what, when I looked up and saw Jim frowning in the doorway.

"Have you forgotten what day this is?" he asked coldly. "I thought we were going fishing!"

Thursday! And I hadn't even called Emily! I followed him into the living room, apologizing and saying I'd call Emily and be ready in ten minutes. I'd been so busy talking to Susan about the Brownies—

"Brownies!" Jim snorted. "From now on, I think I'll spend my day off alone. This place has turned into a regular orphan asylum—"

We thought we were out of the children's hearing, but of course Phyllis heard us. "I'll call Emily," she said and disappeared.

While we were sitting in the boat, *after* Jim had caught a beautiful ten pound silver salmon and was admiring and weighing it, I told him our plans for the gameroom and asked him if he could get a grateful patient to help us paint.

"Sure!" he said, "sounds like a good idea. I'll get Nelson. Now don't change your lure so often and let out more line!"

Friday afternoon Phyllis arrived with her suitcase, announcing that "Mymother" had unselfishly allowed her to stay-all-night so she could help Dr. Jay be a better Brownie father. "He sure has an awful lot to learn," she said blinking at me through her glasses.

At dinner she took one look at the beautiful salmon Jim had caught and said, "I hate fish. Mymother never makes me eat fish. Are you Catholics? Catholics have to eat fish. I choked on a fish bone once—"

"Don't give me any fish, Daddy," our girls chorused.

Jim frowned. "Danes eat fish."

Phyllis asked, "Are you Danes? I'm not. I'm part German and part Irish and part—"

Jim cleared his throat. "Phyllis? I'm sure you will be glad to partake of this fish when you realize it contains calcium, phosphorus, iodine, iron and—"

"Bones." Phyllis' mouth was rebellious.

"—and bones, but fish is a necessary part of a Brownie's diet."

Phyllis blinked. "Do you know the seven kinds of food you need to make you strong and healthy? It says in our Brownie Handbook that we have to eat green and yellow vegetables, meat and eggs, poultry and, my gosh! fish!" She began to eat her salmon.

"Do you know at what temperature you need a sweater, Dr. Jay?"

I know at what temperature Jim boils, so I hastily asked Phyllis to tell us the Health and Safety rules. With her mouth full, she quoted the whole section.

After dinner she said, "Friday night Myfather takes me to a foreign movie. Are you going to take us to a foreign movie, Dr. Jay? They're educational and sometimes they're good—"

Jim said he was sorry but he had to go to the hospital to make rounds.

"What's a round? Could I go? What's a hospital like?"

Jim looked down at her. "Sure, if you want to—"

Heidi said, "Aw, you don't want to go. You just have to sit in the car for hours and hours, and sometimes Daddy forgets all about you. Let's stay here and watch TV."

Phyllis' face lighted up and then stiffened. "Mymother doesn't approve of television. She says—"

Under cover of Mymother's pronouncements, Jim murmured that he didn't approve of Phyllis or Mymother. "By the time I get home I want that paragon in bed. If that's what two years in a Brownie Troop turns out—" He left, slamming the front door behind him.

I suggested that Phyllis telephone her mother and ask permission to watch a carefully chosen TV program.

Phyllis was gone one second and came back to report that as she was a guest in our house, she could watch television.

She was still glued to the set when Jim came home about ten o'clock. He frowned, and I said hastily, "Bedtime" and snapped off the set.

Phyllis looked up at Jim and gave a long, bemused sigh. "Gee. TV's wonderful! When that guy shot that guy, I thought I'd die!"

Jim burst out laughing!

Nelson arrived at eight o'clock Saturday morning and proved to be neither grateful, "I'm not supposed to work Saturday. Can't a man get his sleep?" nor patient, "Get dem children oud of here, get dem oud of here or I qvit!"

At noon Jim and Charlie arrived to help Nelson, and I hastily scooped up Phyllis and Peggy and ours and took off for the farmers' market to buy our pumpkins.

The children were delighted with the howling vendors and pushing, shoving hordes of bargain hunters, darted in and out collecting loot from the kindly farmers and eating shrimps and peanuts and peas out of shells. Enormous pumpkins grinned from every stall, backed by pyramids of glowing apples. "Could we each choose our own pumpkin? Could we buy some apples and duck for apples? Could we each have some chestnuts to roast?"

I weakly said yes to everything, partly because I was trying to shop, but also because I remembered Mother trailing her five to the market every Saturday and patiently waiting while we admired the fat, gleaming horses, stamping their feet with impatience, the rows of vegetables cut in the shapes of flowers, the great banks of brilliant flowers, and the strange and delicious smells dominated by fish, horseradish and gardenias. She also allowed us to eat grapes, sausage, shrimps, cheese, doughnuts, cider, and whatever else we wanted to taste. Nor had the sounds lost their enchantment—the cries of the various nationalities, the swish-swish of vegetables being washed, the bellowing of the irate truck drivers, and the murmur of a crowd intent on shopping.

I was having just as much fun as the children were, wandering up and down admiring the beautiful displays of fall vegetables, buying far more than I needed and amused by watching Phyllis lose her air of detached superiority and behave almost like a child. Her enthusiasm was what prompted me to ask her if she'd like to stay-all-night again so she could go Trick or Treating with us.

"Oh Gee! Could I? Mymother—" she stopped and bit her lip. "It wouldn't encourage vandalism if I went just this once, would it?"

It was almost five when I finally rounded them up. They stood in front of me, each clasping an enormous pumpkin, their faces scarlet with excitement. "Could we get some wienies and have a wienie roast in the outdoor fireplace? Could we, Mother?"

When we got home we found Susan and Charlie and Jim and Nelson sitting around the kitchen table having coffee to celebrate their accomplishments. They were not unlike the Brownies as they all began to talk at once. Susan had found a remnant of monk's cloth which would be more than enough for the curtains, they'd be all finished by Sunday night; Jim and Charlie had found some lumber in Charlie's basement and had made another table and two more benches and put new lighting fixtures in the ceiling; Nelson had finished the painting, all but the red trim although "Wid all dem bookshelves to get around, it was tough!"

After Nelson left, I suggested that Susan and Charlie and Peggy stay for the wienie roast, we had plenty of food because I was incapable of going to the market and bringing home less than a carload.

Phyllis and Mari begged to cook supper, Phyllis had a "neat" recipe she had learned at Brownie Camp.

The atmosphere in the kitchen was even more confusing

than the bread episode, and to me nostalgic because it reminded me of Mother's kitchen—always full of children and animals. The dogs prowled underfoot begging for their supper. Jim and Charlie fought with Peggy and Sally and Heidi over how to cut teeth in pumpkins and sprayed seeds on the floor. Mari and Phyllis made biscuit dough and fought over the menu, while Susan and I picked up the debris and argued about how to turn gunny sacks into costumes, all at the top of our lungs.

Eventually everything was done, the pumpkins were lighted and placed in a leering row on the fence, and we all crouched around the outdoor fireplace roasting Phyllis' recipe. She had stuck the roasting forks through the ends of the wienies and then wound the meat with strips of biscuit dough, which produced a crusty biscuit in the shape of a coiled spring and is far better than the usual damp, gummy roll. The apple and celery salad was *not* improved by the addition of nuts and marshmallows and maraschino cherries, embellishments invented by "Mymother" but who cared when we were having such a "witchy" time eating outdoors and bragging about who had done the most fearsome trick during the good old days of vandalism?

After supper we provided the children with shopping bags and garbed them in gunny sacks with holes cut for arms and heads, and nylon stockings for masks. They marched off down the street, followed by Jim and Charlie, each holding a lighted pumpkin and looking more like ambulant potatoes than ghosts.

While they were gone, Susan and I finished cleaning up the kitchen, still bragging about what different Leaders we were going to be.

"Take tonight for instance." Susan's face was glowing. "I can't remember when I've seen Peggy so happy, and we didn't do one thing but roast wienies—"

We could have Cookouts all the year 'round in the outdoor fireplace, in fact there wasn't anything in the Leader's Guide we couldn't do right in our own neighborhood. "Aren't we glad we volunteered?" we chorused.

When the Trick or Treat-ers finally got back with their bulging shopping bags, Jim and Charlie were tired of being Brownies. "Little monsters!" Charlie grumbled, and Jim said, "All they did was snatch each offering and then make loud and odious comparisons."

Susan and Charlie took Sally back to stay-all-night with Peggy and after they had gone, Jim mused, "I don't remember having this much fun on Hallowe'en. Oh, we tipped over garbage cans and took down street signs, but—"

"It's the Brownies, I tell you. The moment you view things through the eyes of a child, they glow—"

By noon on Sunday, Jim's "glow" was a little dimmed. Phyllis kept following him around, dripping red paint on the floor, while she quoted her Brownie Manual and urged him not to leave things lying around. But even he agreed that it was just as well she stayed for lunch, as it took both of us two hours and a quart of turpentine to get the red paint out of her braids.

It was four o'clock when she finally said, "I think I'd better go home now. I have to see what Mymother and Myfather have been doing while I've been gone." Jim clasped his hands over his head in the victory sign and I drove her home.

When we got in front of her house, she said, "Thanks for the neat time. I'm sorry I didn't get more of a chance to talk to Dr. Jay. He certainly has a lot to learn. Come on in and meet Mymother. She wants to see you."

Feeling slightly uneasy (I fully expected to encounter a tanned edition of Don'ty Dale flourishing a gavel in each hand), I was disarmed when Mymother turned out to be a handsome gray-haired woman whose manner had just a tinge of granting an audience. She thanked me for allowing

Phyllis to spend so much time with a large family and asked me to come in and sit down.

I should have been prepared for the interior, because the exterior was modern with one of those winged roofs that makes a house look like a squatting chicken taking a dust bath. The living room held no hint that a child lived there, or anyone else for that matter. Decorated in varying shades of gray, with a frightening Indian mask scowling over the raised fireplace, it was drear and glacial.

Mr. Bean, an experienced Brownie father, took one look at Phyllis and disappeared into another room. I sat down on a couch reminiscent of a morgue slab. Mrs. Bean sat across from me on an iron-legged basket, erect and graciously waiting.

Phyllis stood between us and fixed her glasses first on her mother and then on me. "Well—go on," she said.

I said I'd enjoyed having Phyllis, she'd been a great help in getting to know the various personalities—

"Phyllis is adept at specific personality references. It is our thinking that the only child, even more than the sibling, benefits by group play."

I blinked. Jim and I had noticed a distinct improvement in our—

Phyllis interrupted. "Mymother doesn't mean our family when she says it is 'our thinking.' She means all those club women."

Without a change of expression, Mymother continued, "—as you may have noticed, Phyllis has developed unusual semantic orientation as a result of our permissive—"

Phyllis broke in, "She means I use big words. I do too except when I'm at your house—"

"—techniques in lieu of authoritarian interpersonal parent-child relationships." Without pausing for breath, and in a well modulated monotone, Mrs. Bean went on and on and on.

Floundering in a maze of "gradients of play, permissive techniques, tensional outlets, somatic complaints, interpersonal relationships and developmental factors," and unable to concentrate because I was supposed to be picking Sally up at Susan's, I finally stood up and said I must go.

Still talking, she held out her hand, "—as chairman of your Troop Committee, it is our responsibility to give you all the necessary cooperation. Please do not hesitate to call on us."

I said our primary need seemed to be more Brownie Leaders in the neighborhood.

This produced another lavaflow, and I *think* she said that previous commitments prevented her from volunteering personally, but she would screen her various organizations for leadership material.

"I told you Mymother was president of just about everything in town," Phyllis called proudly after me as I fled down the steps.

When I stopped at Susan's, I couldn't suppress a grin at the contrast. Susan's living room not only looked lived in, it looked like a gypsy trailer. Charlie was sitting in front of the fire reading aloud and popping corn. Susan and Sally and Peggy, peering out from mounds of monk's cloth, were measuring hems. The coffee table was littered with crayons, drawings, scissors, cardboard and empty coffee cups. The ironing board was set up so Susan could experiment with pressing crayon stencils on the curtains, and it was so cozy and inviting, I felt as if I had been rescued from an iceberg.

Susan pushed a pile of magazines off the couch. "Sit down if you can find a place. The crayon stencils are going to work. I found the idea in a magazine. Where is it? Oh, it's around somewhere." She held up a curtain on which a Brownie grinned from the top of a palm tree. "Charlie's efforts. Isn't he artistic? Now all we have to do is to get the children to draw whatever they like and then we'll press it on. Elegant?"

Sally came over and hugged me. "Mommy! Guess what! Mrs. Blake let me sew on the sewing machine and I made flapjacks and Charlie showed me how to throw them up in the air—"

"A pretty trick which we will teach our Troop and surprise the mothers no end—" Susan said.

"And we wrote a play—" Sally gasped.

"—and if that play doesn't produce new Leaders, nothing will," Charlie said.

"—and do I have to go home now? We've had more fun!" She dove back into the curtains. "See? I know how to hem."

"That's more than Mummy can do." I gestured to Susan to think of something for Peggy and Sally to do elsewhere so I could be frank. "I've just been visiting Mrs. Bean."

Susan suggested that the girls go out and get us some hot coffee.

While they were out of the room, I gave Susan and Charlie a brief description of Bean's Cold Comfort Farm and how semantically oriented I wasn't, told her Mymother promised to pour her various organizations through her presidential sieve and see if she could strain out a few Leaders—

"Shay!" Susan spoke through a mouthful of pins, clawed them out of her mouth, and continued, "Charlie has a ghastly idea which he's been trying to sell me. He got it while he was reading aloud. Do you remember Tom Sawyer and his fence? He thinks we ought to ask two mothers to each meeting as program consultants. It wouldn't be long before they'd volunteer if only to prove that they know more about it than we do."

Charlie grinned. "I hesitate to correct you, Susan my love, but I did not get the idea from reading Tom Sawyer. It came as the result of listening to you tell how many improvements you and Mary were going to make in Mrs. Burton's Troop. Now do me just one favor before you both go whizzing off in all directions. Spend a couple of months Leading and *then* ask two mothers to hear you using bad words in front of children."

7

IT'S NOT FAIR!

*I*T poured and rained every day during November, but from the moment Susan entered the gameroom, we Brownies felt as if we'd turned off from a rutted, rock strewn country road onto a limited access highway.

Susan arrived at noon the Monday after we finished painting the gameroom, laden with curtains and a bulging shopping bag. As she dumped her bundles on the work table she said, "Charlie was pretty bitter when he found me still sewing at three o'clock this morning, but they're finished." She rummaged in the shopping bag. "Sandwiches and a thermos of coffee, so we won't have to stop for lunch; cardboard squares to make the designs roughly the same size; Peggy's hoard of crayons and every pair of scissors in the house; and I brought my iron so we can both press on the designs."

I too had not been idle. I'd stayed up until twelve o'clock Sunday night studying Mrs. Burton's individual records of each child so I'd know what idiosyncrasies to expect. Monday morning I'd bought two potted red geraniums for each window sill to accent the red trim and disguise the morbid

light wells; had turned on the new overhead lights and built
a roaring fire in the fireplace; had divided the lower shelves
of the bookcase into sections and had lettered a Brownie's
name on each section; and had also persuaded Vi and Murph
to give me enough empty cigar boxes so each Brownie could
have one to keep her treasures in.

Susan smiled appreciatively around the long room. "Looks
mighty festive. You know, I'm really looking forward to this.
Aside from occasional substitute teaching, it's been quite a
spell since this old firehorse answered the bell." She reached
into her shopping bag again. "Oh yes. I've been rooting
through the Leader's Guide and the various How To Do
books and made a list of crafts."

As I read the long list ranging from abacus to zoo, I asked
her if some of them weren't a little complicated for fat fingers.

She shook her head. "I don't think so. Whether we like
it or not, Christmas is upon us. The stores are already bediz-
ened with trees and bells and ornaments, and you can be
sure our dear little kiddies have seen them. I wonder when
it will occur to the merchants to put up their Christmas
decorations on New Year's Day so they can begin January
2nd working us up into a lather. 'Remember, only three hundred shopping days until Christmas!' Oh well, we can't go
outdoors, so I suppose we should be thankful."

We set the tables with crayons, pencils, scissors and a
cigar box at each place and then sat down in front of the fire,
ostensibly to go over the individual records while we ate
our lunch, but actually to compare notes on how *darling* our
offspring were compared to all the other Brownies.

I thought Mari was bossy until I met Madame President.
Compared to Phyllis, Mari was a cringing wardheeler. Susan
laughed. She and Charlie had spent most of one summer
entertaining Phyllis. A more complacent little body, they'd
never seen. Permissive techniques! Just plain bad manners

was more like it. They'd had to watch Phyllis like a hawk or she'd have snatched everything Peggy owned and taken it home. Peggy was so shy and gentle and yet for an only child, she was amazingly unselfish. Yes, Sally was like that, sweet and gentle and kind—

We were still congratulating one another on our own perfect specimens and how noble we were to be Brownie Leaders, thus enabling less fortunate children to have the benefit of our remarkable maternal influence, when the door burst open and in catapulted Mari, followed by the whole tribe of soaking wet, howling savages who took one look at the fresh paint and began rushing around feeling it, hoping it was still wet.

"Lookit the pretty red flars!—Lookit the fire!—Gee! Yellow's my favorite color! Lookit, here's my name on the bookcase!" In spite of the overpowering odor of Juicy Fruit Gum mingled with wet wool blanket, their enthusiasm was infectious, and Susan and I beamed at them and then at one another. "Aren't they *darlings!*"

Phyllis yelled, "QUIET! Can't you see Mrs. Blake's here?" and ordered them to go out and hang up their coats. I had just rolled my eyes at Susan with a "see what I mean?" expression, when I heard a peacock's scream from my cringing wardheeler, followed by, "I guess my father made those boxes. Now PUT YOUR GALOSHES AWAY!"

Susan chuckled, "I wish you could see your face—"

Her grin faded when they sat down at the table and her own shy, self-sacrificing Peggy took one look at the boxes of crayons, yelled, "Hey! Those are mine!" and swept them into her lap.

With many glances at Susan, Madame President was even more abrupt than usual. Also there was an atmosphere of watchful haste from the children which I should have realized meant that they were trying to hide something, but which I foolishly attributed to the presence of a new Leader.

It wasn't until roll call and they rattled off their names like a machine gun, that I knew what they were trying to cover —two new faces. Beside Sumiko sat a smaller Japanese edition with even shinier black bangs. Beside Patty sat a slightly shorter child with her eyes glued to a book.

I murmured this discovery to Susan who said, "Who are they?"

While they were stuffing down their treat, I walked over and asked Phyllis if she would like to introduce us to her guests. She said briefly, "They aren't guests. They're new Brownies. They're little sisters" and gave me a hard look.

"Oh I'm afraid not. The Troop is too full—" Immediately I was drowned out by wails of, "It's not fair—Mari has two sisters—what about Peggy—it's not fair—"

I retired to my corner and Susan murmured, "This is deliberate goat-getting." She took the Troop list and stood up.

"We're going to play a game. It's called Touch." Her eyes ranged around the circle of glowering faces. Patty, as usual, was reading. Susan said, "Patty? You choose one Team and—" she looked at Durdey who was holding Sally's hand and looking passively pretty. "Dierdre? You choose the other Team."

Durdey's enormous blue eyes widened, she gulped and said, "Thally? You choothe." Between them, they managed to choose a Team consisting of the younger members of the Troop.

Phyllis came storming over. "Mrs. Blake, I don't know whether you realize it, but I'm President. I always choose the Teams."

"Not today you don't," Susan said briefly and turned back to the startled Teams. "When I say Touch, everybody runs over and touches whatever I have named. The first Team with all players back in line scores one point. There will be eight points. The Team with the largest number of points wins. Ready? Touch the doorknob."

Under the scuffling rush to the doorknob, Susan asked me how long Phyllis had been president. I told her I hadn't the faintest idea. According to Mrs. Burton's records, they held elections once a month because "Mymother" wished them to learn Robert's Rules of Order, but judging by the Troop's behavior, Phyllis was well into her twentieth term of office.

Susan glanced up, marked D-1 on a piece of paper, said to the panting teams, "Touch the floor next to the farthest corner of the bookcase," and added, "What about having elections at the next meeting?"

Due to the fact that the littler ones were able to skitter around the larger ones, Durdey's Team scored six points and won. This caused screams of rage from the fourth grade and howls of "It's not fair—"

Susan said, "It is fair and from now on we always play fair." She added in a throaty voice, "Don't forget, Girl Scouts are honorable." They gulped and subsided.

"Now, we will divide up into grades, the fourth grade at the old table and the third grade at the new table. We will make our own designs for our curtains. You may draw anything you like." She gave a brief and clear description of crayon designs applied to curtains.

During this explanation, Phyllis had been giving Susan cruel looks and whispering to the Brownie on either side of her. She waited until Susan had finished and led a chorus of, "We did it in school."

Susan said, "Did you?" A flicker of disappointment crossed her face.

Immediately I took up the cudgels in her defense and made quite a speech, telling them how hard and late Susan had worked on *their* curtains and how we had spent all day Saturday and Sunday painting *their* gameroom. They looked so serious and downcast that I got carried away. "From now on, this is *your* room. You may play down here whenever you like and leave your things in your own box on your own shelf when you go home."

Mine said, "Mo-ther-r-r" and looked embarrassed, but the rest of them cheered up and fell to with a will, drawing dinosaurs with pink spines, huge snarling animals crouched on flowered twigs, and modern cubes and squiggles which they insisted were not pictures of anything but were how they felt. Phyllis and her clack produced pictures of crabby ladies which looked suspiciously like their Leaders. However, they seemed to be enjoying themselves. While they were drawing, Susan and I were pressing, and by five o'clock the curtains were all edged. When we hung them up, they were pronounced "beeautiful" and "just neat!"

They had put on their coats and were making their Good-night Tunnel when I felt a tug and looked down to see Sumiko flanked by her little sister. "This is Kaziko. I can't be a Brownie if Kaziko can't come too. My mother works and I have to take care of her."

Patty said, "My Mom said if you had Mari and Sally and Heidi, she didn't see why I couldn't bring Betty—she's in the second grade—"

I hesitated, glanced at Susan who nodded and said, "Sure, why not? The more the merrier."

When Jim came home, we took him down to show him our new curtains. He pronounced them much more attractive than the primitive handblocked linen which Mother had tried to make him buy in the decorator's shop.

That night at dinner the girls were telling about the meeting and I was extolling the virtues of Susan's teacher spell, when Heidi said, "That lady came to school again today. She took me out of my room and asked me a whole bunch of dumb questions and made me play with blocks, and—"

"What lady?" Jim asked.

"Oh, that lady in the blue suit."

Both Jim and I tried to pry additional information out of

her, but Heidi, who was perfectly capable of giving a hair-by-hair description of any animal she encountered, seemed incapable of further details.

"Was it the school nurse?" Mari asked.

"No, dumby, it wasn't Miss McMonigle. Everybody knows Miss McMonigle."

"Was it the art teacher?" Sally asked.

"No, dopey, it wasn't Miss Drury. She has squeaky shoes."

"Who was it?" Jim asked.

Heidi sighed. "I *told* you, Daddy, she's that lady in the blue suit. Can I have some more salad?"

Each afternoon the girls brought home more and more Brownies to play in the gameroom. Heidi clattered downstairs after them, flanked by her dogs, but reappeared almost immediately, grumbling, "Just wait 'til I'm a Brownie. I'll show those kids—" and retired to the porch over the Lake to throw her ball for Spot and Dagmar.

Each night at dinner when the girls told another tale of Brownie prowess, Heidi countered with a story of that lady in the blue suit. "Today she asked me, 'What's twelve times twelve.' Honestly! Everybody knows that twelve times twelve is a hundred and forty-four."

Now and then during the day when I was dusting or making the beds, "that lady in the blue suit" would cross my mind, but I dismissed her as someone from the principal's office, or a new teacher with whom Heidi was unfamiliar.

Thursday morning Jim said he wouldn't be home for lunch. He was going to stay at the office and work up some charts.

Heidi asked, "What's the matter, Daddy? Is it because those girls talk about the Brownies all the time?"

Jim ruffled her hair. "Heavens, no. You can talk about the Brownies all you want to. It's just that I have some charts to get out of the way, and I might as well do it at the office."

After they left, I called Susan and suggested that we hurry up and get our work done and go downtown for lunch and buy a baby present for Mrs. Burton.

We spent most of our time wandering around the gift sections seeing what brilliant ideas they had to offer that a Brownie could make, became thoroughly discouraged, and then spent an hour in the baby department choosing an appropriate offering for young David Burton. We stopped on the way home to deliver our presents.

Mrs. Burton, flushed with pride, was delighted with our unexpected visit. She showed us young David, a wrinkled pink gentleman snuggled in a blue blanket just like the one we had purchased, who had hands like curled peony buds and a satiny neck smelling more delicious than any perfume in the world, and eyes which he refused to open in spite of our drooling admiration.

Susan's and my eyes filled with jealous tears as Mrs. Burton cradled David in her arms. "You can't imagine what it's like to have a baby of your very own!" Her face was brooding and defenseless with love. She looked up and smiled. "Tell me, how are you getting along with my Brownies?"

While Susan described, in dry and realistic terms, her first encounter with the Troop, I looked around Mrs. Burton's small, immaculate living room and wondered how on earth she had corralled sixteen exuberant Brownies in such a small space.

I said as much and Mrs. Burton sighed, "I did the best I could, and of course we went outdoors every chance we got, but it was hard, especially in winter."

"How did you get into that trap in the first place?" Susan asked.

Mrs. Burton grinned. "I really didn't have enough to do. David wouldn't let me work, and I wanted children so much. Of course I was a Girl Scout—"

While she and Susan vied with one another in telling tales

of their youthful Scout Troops, I had the sensation which I wore all the time I was a Brownie Leader and still wear, that of being an island, entirely surrounded by a body of ex-Scouts.

That night I found that I wasn't the only island. Jim too felt entirely surrounded.

"Do you realize that we haven't had an adult to dinner since school started?" Jim asked.

I knew it only too well, but I had a one-track mind and just as soon as I felt the Brownies were under control, which they obviously were going to be soon, thanks to Susan's teacher spell, we'd have dinner guests every night in the week if he liked.

Jim prowled around the living room. "I thought you were going to improve your mind."

I was and I still had every intention of doing it. Actually it was being improved. The Brownies asked so many questions—

Jim picked up a Medical Journal and leafed through it. "Many of my neurotic patients are women who haven't faced the fact that their children have to grow up. You wouldn't be one of those, would you?"

Mercy no. That was one of the prime reasons I was concentrating on being a good Leader. I expected to learn by observing other children, just how much responsibility to give ours, and just where it was advisable to draw the line between permissive and disciplinary techniques.

"I suppose it's a good idea, but I'd like to have you to myself once in a while." Jim picked up the Medical Journal and went upstairs.

The next day I gave the children their supper early and had a discussion. I told them that we weren't being fair to Daddy. He was tired when he came home and from now on we were going to be considerate and not talk so much about the Brownies at dinner.

They looked bewildered. "What else will we talk about?" Sally asked.

Oh, we'd ask Daddy to tell us about being a doctor, and ask him to tell us jokes, and we'd tell him about school, but no Brownies.

"Phyllis says—" Mari began and Heidi said, "Daddy and I are both sick of Phyllis and sicker of those old Brownies."

Jim purred at the sight of steak and kidney pie, and spinach béchamel, and pronounced the cheesecake even better than his mother used to make. Then he asked me about the Brownies.

I said we had a new household rule. No discussion of Brownies after five o'clock.

He looked bewildered. "Why not?" and then grinned and gave me a special hug and kiss and told me I was illogical but a cozy homemaker.

The following Monday was election day. Phyllis had obviously organized her cohorts on the way to the meeting; they filed into the room, said, "Hi, Mrs. Jay, hi, Mrs. Blake," and sat down.

Phyllis said, "We won't have the secretary or treasurer's report, or roll call, or collect the dues, until after the election." There was subdued giggling while Phyllis moved around behind each one and carried on a campaign of threats and promises worthy of Tammany. "Jennie, I'll take back my pink shell—Cherie, I'll tell teacher what you wrote in that note—Jane, you want to be Treasurer, don't you?"

With many warning looks and muttered threats, Phyllis passed out the pencils and the voting slips. She announced the slate, counted the votes and not only was re-elected, but her slate was carried unanimously.

She turned to us with a sneer. "See? I'm still President."

"This is a democracy, and in a democracy everyone votes the way she wants to. Do you think your election was fair?" Susan asked.

Phyllis blinked at her for a few moments, scuffed her toe around in a circle, and then said, "A democracy is fair. My mother told me all about it. If I went upstairs and stayed in the kitchen while they voted, would that be fair? Would it, Mrs. Jay?"

I said I didn't think such radical methods were necessary but Phyllis turned to the Troop, told them they could vote for anybody they wanted to, and stalked out of the room.

The Brownies gave us cruel looks, stuck out their chins, and muttered among themselves, but they voted. When the votes were counted, Mari was elected president and Peggy Blake vice-president. The rest of the slate remained the same.

This was manifestly unfair, but Susan said to let it go, it was obviously a compromise and not an entire change of party.

Phyllis came back into the room, looked at the slate, nodded, and sat down next to Mari to assume the role of Secretary of State. "Now open the meeting, now ask for the secretary's report, now the treasurer—"

Jane was eagerly collecting the dues when I felt a plucking at my skirt. I looked down to find a small dusty child carrying a large green felt bag, several books and what appeared to be a fishnet. She said, "Are you the new Brownie Lady? Here, hold this—" She handed me a large black beetle which scratched furiously as my fist closed around him. "Don't let him go, he is a coleopterous."

The Brownies called, "Hi, Diana, you finally decided to come—" and went on with their meeting.

Diana unfastened one button, and coat, bag, books and net cascaded to the floor. She went on speaking in the same soft voice, "He has two pairs of wings called elytra, the outside pair is hard and the inside pair is soft—"

"Diana what?" I asked. "What is your name?"

"—and I found him under a rock on the way and I'm going to take him home so my father can tell me more about him—"

Susan knelt down and put her hands on Diana's small shoulders. "Pause for breath, my friend, and tell us your last name."

"—Lamson and his antenna are hairy and his legs are too—" Diana wandered toward the third grade table trailing clothes and the four stages of the beetle behind her.

I was still holding the resentful beetle, so I followed Diana and leaned down. "Diana? Are you a Brownie?"

She nodded, her enormous black eyes staring at a point just beyond my left shoulder. "—the first stage is the egg, and then the grub which looks like a worm only it has a big head. Some beetles live in houses and some live—"

The beetle in my hand gave a convulsive jerk and pinched. "This beetle doesn't like to live with me, so you hold him."

Diana took the beetle and examined him carefully as she put one leg over the end of the bench. "See his wings? He—"

Phyllis said, "Don't pay any attention to Diana. She's a Brownie, but she hardly ever remembers to come to the meetings. She just talks about bugs. Her father's a professor and her mother is too. Her intelligence quotient is unusually high, that means she's a genius."

In Phyllis' exact tone, Mari snapped, "SIDDOWN, DIANA."

Diana remained as isolated from the group as if she were alone on a rock with her beetle, while the Troop boiled around her playing squat tag.

"Diana's name *was* on Mrs. Burton's list. I thought she'd moved away. And Angela was supposed to move away too, but Mari says her father isn't going. Susan, now there are twenty! What will the Council say?" I asked Susan under cover of the noise.

Susan was busily removing various objects from her capacious shopping bag. "They won't say anything because they won't know, and what they don't know can't hurt them."

"But we'll have to register them and have Investiture—"

"Relax. We'll take care of that when we come to it. One of the first things you have to learn when you are herding small children is, let nature take its course. Always have a plan, because they become homicidal when they're bored. If your plan doesn't work out, try, try again. How do you like this?" She held up a clothes hanger from which hung suspended a gingham laundry bag blanket-stitched together. "It didn't cost anything and I think it's rather sweet." She produced a kitchen matchbox covered with metallic paper and decorated with a picture of a flying duck, "A present for Daddy." Next came an oatmeal carton covered with wallpaper with a brass ring glued to the top and a piece of yarn sticking through the ring. "This my crafty companion, is a knitting bag for Mother. They're just a beginning, but believe me, any exit in case of fire."

I was overwhelmed, but I regret to say the Brownies did not share my enthusiasm. They examined the presents, shook their heads, muttered, "My Mommy uses a laundry basket," "My Mom doesn't even know how to knit," "My Dad has a lighter." These were the more charitable comments.

I was all for banging their ungrateful little heads together, but Susan shrugged. "They don't have to like them, the trick is to emulate the department stores and get them thinking in terms of Christmas instead of goat-getting. Why don't you fix up a batch of gardening presents for the next meeting. You know, a planter, a terrarium, a potted bulb—things like that. In the meantime—" she raised her voice slightly, "Suppose you all sit down and write a list of things you'd like to get for Christmas. Maybe we'll get some good ideas from your lists."

Instantly the critical atmosphere disappeared and they

began to write like mad, occasionally resting their chins on their hands and gazing off into space while televisions of sugar plums danced through their little pigheads.

We walked around the table reading the lists: Brownie wallet, Brownie shorts, Brownie camping kit, Brownie T shirt, Brownie sweater, Brownie socks—nothing that was not Brownie.

"A fat lot of help they are," I muttered.

"They are. Indeed they are. Do you realize that our Christmas shopping will take about fifteen minutes? One quick trip to the Girl Scout desk, charge it, and we're through."

Heidi's was not a list. It was a letter:

> Dear Santy Claus:
>   I want two of Johnny's rabbits, two hamsters, two kittens, and a new puppy.
>
>   Heidi

I said maybe Santa Claus didn't have hamsters, and she said, "If he brings me one single Brownie thing, I won't ever write to him again." (And she never did.)

I spent hours making a terrarium with tiny orange toadstools, bits of moss and seedling firs nestling at the bottom of a peanut butter jar; a planter with rocks and driftwood and "baby's tears" curled over the edge; a pot of crocuses from the garden; and I even gave up two of my cherished hyacinths whose fat buds already showed promise of waxy, perfumed blooms.

The Brownies examined them, even admired them half-heartedly, but said they didn't think their mothers would like them—they'd already made them in school.

"We've only got six or seven meetings left. What do we do now?" I asked Susan.

"We keep right on making samples and lining them up on the mantel so they'll get used to seeing them around. In the meantime we sing Jingle Bells and read The Night Before Christmas and try to whip up spirit."

We sang Jingle Bells and looked at Christmas catalogs and read The Night Before Christmas. They didn't seem to mind, but neither did they rush toward the tempting merchandise displayed on the mantel.

The last Monday in November, Emily came bounding into the meeting followed by her inseparable chums Judy and Jody. "Hi, Mrs. Jay and Mrs. Blake. Could we talk to the Brownies for a minute?"

We nodded and the Brownies sat in openmouthed adoration while Emily explained her great big Community Christmas project and asked them how they'd like to help make ours the best Community Christmas in the whole city.

Would they! They squealed with delight and crowded around Emily and Jody and Judy.

Well! Emily and Judy and Jody had attended this meeting at school where a guy talked about decorating the trees outdoors instead of chopping down our National Forest and had said it was up to every student to help make this the Christmasiest city in the whole U-nited States.

Wow! What a neat idea!

"So-o-o—we had a meeting of our Senior Troop and voted to have ours the very best community and make candy wreaths out of coathangers—Do you have any old coathangers, Mrs. Jay?—and sell them for $2.00—Would you like to buy some, Mrs. Jay?—so we can earn enough money to buy lights and decorations for our Community Tree. Would you guys like to string cranberries, enough for that great big tree down by the pond?"

Oh Boy! They'd string hot coals if Emily asked them to.

"—and popcorn? Remember, it's kind of hard to string—"

Who cares? They were popping up and down like corn in a hot popper at that moment.

"—and the Boy Scouts are going to collect toys and take

them up to the fire station and your daddies are going to help paint them and give them to poor children. Would you like to help by giving your old toys?"

They'd rather give old toys than get new ones.

Emily sighed. "Gosh, I'm glad. I knew I could count on you. Brownies always help other people, especially those at home." She winked at me. "Do you suppose we could make our wreaths down here, Mrs. Jay? We'd put everything away, but it would sure be great to work on these tables."

Sure. They could work any day but Monday.

Emily hugged me. "I told the girls you'd say that. You're just the greatest."

During Emily's plea for help, Jody and Judy had wandered over to the fireplace and were examining the display on the mantel. Judy, or Jody, I never can tell them apart, said, "Hey, Em. Commere and look. Are these ever cute!"

Emily exclaimed and admired each and every object. "I remember when we used to make presents just like these. Mom was just thrilled, Dad was too. They still have most of 'em." She turned to the awestricken Troop. "You'd better hurry up and get these presents made so you'll have plenty of time to help us. Say, we've gotta go. We've got to call on every single store in the shopping district." She linked arms with Jody and Judy, they gave a smart salute, and sauntered out the door.

The Brownies made a rush for the mantel. "I want to make a knitting bag—me too—I want to make a planter—me too—"

That night at dinner Mari and Sally were babbling about the Community Christmas tree and their presents and who would give what to who, when Heidi said, "I had a perfectly good Christmas surprise for you and Daddy, but that lady in the blue suit ruined it." She dug in the pocket of her jeans and handed Jim a grubby envelope.

Jim read it, whistled, and handed it to me.

It was a communication from the Child Guidance Center, saying that Heidi was too advanced for the first grade and that from now on she would be in the second grade.

I read this world-shaking announcement aloud and we all kissed Heidi and hugged her and told her how proud we were. Mari said joyfully, "Just think! Now you can be a Brownie!"

Heidi's eyes glinted. "What if I don't want to?"

8

SANTA'S WORKSHOP

OUR Community Project went on night and day from December first until December twenty-third. At times Jim and I were forced to retire to our bedroom and lock the door, where Jim sang, "Christmas comes but once a year, Hurray, hurray, hurray." At others he said, "Until I became a Girl Scout, I didn't realize what Christmas could mean."

The first pair of badged and beribboned Boy Scouts who came to the door after dinner to collect toys for the fire station, reduced our daughters to a giggling clot of admiration. I called Jim to deal with his sex, they carried off the tricycles, bicycles and battered wagons from the terrace, and had I not used force, he would have given them every toy the girls possessed. "I was a Boy Scout and I remember how tough it was to collect things," he said, his eyes hungrily following these male Scouts.

At the twenty-second pair of Boy Scouts who came to the door after dinner to collect toys, his eyes were no longer hungry. "Don't those Scouts have anything to do but ring doorbells? When I was a boy, I had homework."

Mrs. Bean called each evening that first week. "As Chairman of our Community Christmas Project and of your Troop Committee, I'd like to ask your cooperation. Could you and your Brownies produce one hundred and twenty-five yards of cranberries and one hundred and twenty-five yards of popcorn by December twentieth at the latest?"

"Well—yes—I think so—"

"Could you and your Brownies produce one hundred metallic paper ornaments by December twentieth at the latest? I have two Girl Scout Troops on this project also. They will deliver the materials—"

"Could you and your Brownies produce twenty-five soup cans painted with luminous paint? I have two Girl Scout Troops on this project also. They will bring you a sample."

"Could the Girl Scouts use your gameroom as headquarters for their projects? They will see that it is left in order at all times."

As I reported each new request to Jim, he said, "Hasn't that woman ever heard of child-labor laws?" and "What did Mrs. Bean do before she discovered you?"

"Could Dr. Jay give at least one night a week at the fire station rehabilitating toys? I have twenty-five fathers on this project, and twenty-five mothers dressing dolls, but we have to have our boxes completed and ready for delivery by the twentieth of December at the latest."

Jim snarled, "Tell her I have to make house calls."

But that same evening Charlie Blake called and asked for Jim. I listened to a long, laughing, masculine conversation consisting of "Sure thing, Charlie, glad to help. Ha-ha. Mary can always transfer any calls up there—ha—ha. Any time, any time. Be up right away." He went to the hall closet, grabbed his coat, said to transfer his calls to the fire station, he was going up to help good old Charlie paint toys.

He came home from that house call at twelve o'clock, saying he didn't realize what fancy new equipment those firemen had. There'd been a couple of alarms, he and Charlie had ridden with the Chief, and what with one thing and another, he supposed it was a little late. "What've you been doing?" He grinned foolishly.

"Popping corn and trying to prevent your patients from finding out that Doctor was chasing fires," I answered bitterly.

And from that night on, Jim could usually be found at the fire station.

Meanwhile the gameroom became a seething mass of Senior Girl Scouts, Girl Scouts and Brownies, busily fashioning elaborate metallic ornaments, making candy wreaths, and painting soup cans while the radio blatted Christmas carols.

There was one bright star in all this hectic activity. I never laid eyes on a Brownie except on Monday afternoon. They were much too busy breathing down the necks of "those girls" and answering the telephone which was more insistent than the Salvation Army bells.

Susan and I spent most afternoons, and most evenings, together, hating Mrs. Bean and making popcorn. "There must be some easier way to do this," Susan said sorting the few white kernels out of the mass of little black bullets. "Let's go up and ask Vi if she knows where to buy commercial popcorn."

Vi said, "Hey, Murph, can't we get Mrs. Jay and Mrs. Blake some of those drums of commercial popcorn?" Murph said, "Sure, easiest thing in the world." Vi turned back to us. "I'll tell you what, Murph and I'll furnish the popcorn, might even string some for you if you'll promise not to tell Mrs. Bean. She's doing a good job, but she's sure got the neighborhood in an uproar."

The next afternoon, Murph delivered four enormous drums of popcorn, white and tough and easy to string. He glanced in the gameroom where Emily's Seniors, hindered by most of our Troop, were stringing cellophane-wrapped taffy on wires. "Well, well. Santa's workshop. What are you girls doing?"

Emily showed him how to pull a coathanger into a circle, cover it with green tissue paper, and wind it with vari-colored candies. "Gosh, the candy costs so much, we're only clearing about twenty-five cents a wreath. I hope we make enough to finish the ornaments."

Murph's kindly face crinkled into a smile. "Easiest thing in the world. Drop into the wholesale house, pick you up a couple of drums and have 'em down here tomorrow. Won't cost you a cent."

Emily hugged him and said he was the greatest, just the greatest, and the girls broke into "Three cheers for Vi and Mu-u-rph, Vi-i, and Murph."

Murph looked down at the floor, wound his hands together and said, "Aw, cut it out. Vi and I figure the least we can do is to furnish the materials, when you kids do all the work. Just let us know when you need something." He turned to me. "Vi says you have to string cranberries. How many do you figure you'll need?"

I told him I hadn't the faintest idea, but we were starting Monday at the Troop meeting.

"Sure thing. Get you a case and have 'em down here Monday morning."

Monday, Susan and I discovered that Vi and Murph weren't the only merchants in our little shopping area imbued with the spirit of giving. Minnie'd taken her school shoes to Mr. Carlson, and he was so busy! He was going to repair and shine every single pair of shoes that was collected for the fire station Christmas boxes. Gloria's mother was making a fruit cake and a box of cookies for every single box. Boy! Was she ever busy. Patty had taken her Dad's pants to Mr. Doran, and he and Mrs. Doran were going to clean and press all the clothes. Phyllis had been to the drugstore to get Mymother some more notepaper, and guess what! Mr. Riddell was furnishing the lights for the big tree at cost, so Emily's Troop wouldn't have to earn so much money. The Ten Cent Store, the Beauty Parlor, the Coffee Shop, all had a project, so ours would be the best Community in the whole U-nited States! Boy! They sure felt Christmasy now.

From my nest of cranberries, I muttered to Susan, "Notepaper! Mrs. Bean called last night and said the merchants were cooperative! Cooperative! Has she the faintest idea how much work she dreams up for other people to do? Oh no. All she does is sit at the telephone and make lists while other people do all the work."

"And you wouldn't trade jobs with her for all the tea in China." Susan nodded toward the Brownies who were stringing cranberries, making dish gardens, featherstitching laundry bags, and covering matchboxes and oatmeal cartons, while Patty read aloud Hans Christian Andersen's Fir Tree. Reflected on their intent faces were the changing moods of the story, sympathy for the fir who didn't like to be called little, longing for the forest with its snow and furry animals, vengeance for the cruel woodchoppers, and trembling excitement at the description of Christmas eve.

"Here you are awash with eager children, including hers, while she sits alone with her lists. Still want to trade?" Susan added another string to the mound of cranberries and wiped her crimson fingers on her apron. "I'll string cranberries twenty-four hours a day if necessary for the privilege of seeing Peggy busy and happy instead of a forlorn only child wandering around trying to whip up an appetite for Christmas."

I said that actually, with Emily's built-in baby sitters, I'd had more leisure than ever before. Between Emily's wreaths, which I intended to give to the various members of my own family, and the girls' Brownie lists, I hadn't decided what to do about Heidi's letter, but Johnny's rabbits were obviously a must, and except for some steelhead flies which I intended to make while Jim was up at the fire station cavorting with Charlie, I had everything done.

"Are you going to make Christmas cookies this year?" Susan asked.

"Oh yes. It's a family custom, and besides I always make a box for each of the Neglected Ones."

"Who's that?" Susan asked.

It was a group of doctors' wives I'd belonged to ever since I was first married. I'd skipped the September meeting but had gone to the October, where they'd suggested so many symptoms that I didn't know whether I was strong enough to be a Brownie Leader, and at the November meeting I gave them such a sales talk on the Girl Scouts, they'd made me chairman of the spring garden sale, which meant transplanting millions of chrysanthemums.

"Sounds ghastly," Susan said. "I'd offer to help you, but you know me, can't tell a thistle from a tulip and glad of it."

"Oh well, it's not until March." I glanced over at the Brownies who were grinding their teeth with rage at those mean old children who threw out that darling little fir tree, and were squashing their cranberries in the process.

Susan rescued the cranberries and I said, "How would you like to put on your coats and go outdoors to see what else we can find for your dish gardens. It's stopped raining."

The sew-ers elected to stay with Susan, and the gardeners followed me out into the yard.

While the Brownies ranged back and forth on the soggy grass hunting for seedlings, seed pods, ferns and moss, I gazed at the snow-covered Cascade Range and our glistening Great White Father and thought of how un-Christmasy our climate really was. Blossoms, small and shriveled, clung to the rosebushes, the shaggy heads of chrysanthemums hung over and dripped tears on the winter pansies, Michaelmas daisies the clear blue of a spring sky bravely put forth new daisies which were beaten to the ground by the rain and lay there, cold and miserable.

I positively longed for the winters I knew as a child. I could almost hear the squeak of snow crunching under shiny black overshoes, could almost taste the long icicles plucked from the eaves, and could see the delicate tracery of frost on the window panes.

Our poor little children would never know the thrill of snow stretching as far as eye could see, broken only by turquoise blue shadows and the black arms of winter trees. They knew only varying shades of green. They would never feel the tingling excitement of riding in a sleigh, wrapped to the eyes in blankets, while they listened to the clop, clop, clop of hooves and watched the steam rise from the horses' brown flanks. They would never hear the creak of runners on dry snow, or the jangle of sleighbells. The only sleighbells our daughters had ever heard were the string Jim and I shook under their windows Christmas eve so they could fall asleep knowing Santa Claus was coming. Why didn't "Father" move over just this once and let my Brownies share his soft white blanket of snow?

My reverie was broken by Minnie's call, "Mrs. Jay? Commere and lookit!" She was kneeling beside the perennial bed, cradling three yellow winter pansies in her hands. "They're still blooming and it's nearly Christmas." She looked up at me. "In North Dakota where we used to live, there weren't any flowers in winter. Just snow. Sometimes it was so cold we couldn't even go outdoors. Boy! I love this place, don't you?"

Then, and only then, did I remember my chilblains and my frostbitten nose and ears and the winters when the mercury just went down into the bulb and stayed and we couldn't go outdoors for weeks at a time.

As I watched Minnie holding the pansies with such joy in her solemn little face, I was haunted by an increasing sense of helplessness. Susan was wonderful and her playground techniques produced order, but we were *not* doing what we were supposed to do as Leaders of a Brownie Troop. We were *not* getting to know each child we worked with so that belonging to our Troop was giving her the kind of companionship she needed. I knew Minnie's mother worked the night shift which meant she had to leave home at four o'clock and couldn't return until midnight. This meant that Minnie had to do all the housework, help her brother with his paper route and then get dinner. Minnie was also a straight A student and her face showed unmistakable signs of strain. I remembered Mrs. Burton's comment on Minnie —"This child has too much responsibility at home, is too conscientious in school, and seldom plays. Watch her, she has a tendency to be withdrawn." Minnie actually needed special attention and affection and yet I had not had time to speak especially to her for three weeks.

Cherie, the French child with the deft fingers, seldom had a chance to play, she was so busy helping the other children. And yet basically she was a joyous child, if we only had time to bring her out.

Patty had blossomed visibly since we'd asked her to read aloud, and she had become more friendly since she had taken to coming home with our children after school. Reading all the time was probably an escape rather than a pleasure to a child as tall and self-conscious as Patty.

Ever since Katie had been elected President, at the end of Mari's "term," she had fought constantly with Phyllis, was even more disagreeable and dictatorial, and felt called upon to torture the younger children by sneering at their Christmas presents.

As a matter of fact I was rapidly developing a psychic block against the complacent, tactless ten-year-old. I'd had all I could do to refrain from commenting when Phyllis told me how Mymother made piecrust and served frozen TV dinners; when Gloria insisted that her mother's dry as dust bakery cookies were better than homemade; when Katie said to me, a mining engineer's daughter, "That's not decomposed granite, that's pyrite. We had it in school." I was even rebelling against Mari's constant self-righteous bossing.

However, the bossing and quoting of the Handbook was not nearly as hard to bear as the new Sweet Reason which was coming out in the older girls like measles.

Sweet Reason had appeared as a result of their admiration for Emily's Senior Troop. The Seniors had just completed their Leader in Training program and kept telling the fourth-graders that they were going to Fly Up pretty soon and turn into Intermediates and it was therefore necessary for them to begin learning their Tenderfoot requirements and to live by the Girl Scout Laws.

As a result of these admonitions, Katie insisted that we spend one meeting reading aloud the Girl Scout Promise, the Girl Scout Laws, and the Tenderfoot requirements. After we had all contributed to a long rambling discussion as to what these salutary documents meant, the budding "tenderfeet"—as our Troop called them, with blithe inaccuracy— cited instances of forlorn little children they knew who were *not* Brownie Scouts and were therefore *dis*honorable, *dis*loyal, *un*helpful, *un*friendly, *un*kind to animals, *dis*obedient, *dis*agreeable, and spendthrift. The examples they gave of children who were *un*clean in thought, word and deed almost turned Susan's and my hair white.

It was after this discussion that the ten-year-olds began to come out in spots. No longer did Mari yell, "Put your coat on right this minute or I'll tell Mother." Instead, in a sickly sweet voice, she interpreted whatever I asked the other children to do.

When I reminded Heidi to feed the dogs, Mari said, "Honey, you mustn't forget to feed your animals. Animals can't tell you what they want. A Girl Scout is kind to animals."

When Sally said, as she did almost every afternoon, "Durdey makes me sick. She won't even pretend. All she does is just sit there and rock her doll," Mari said, "Honey, a Girl Scout is loyal."

When I snapped, "Pick up your things," Mari said, "Honey, a Girl Scout is Cheerful."

Jim was sweetly reminded to be Friendly when the paper boy called at dinnertime to "collect for the Times" and Useful when I suggested that he hang up his coat instead of tossing it over the banister. In fact, Mari had become so cloyingly, sickeningly sweet that Jim said, "What's come over Firstborn anyway? Is she planning to become a nun?"

"No. Just a Girl Scout," I said, praying that time plus a muzzle would take me through this phase.

My thoughts were interrupted by a small circle of glowing faces. "Lookit, Mrs. Jay! Lookit what I found! A teeny, weeny Christmas tree for my terrarium! Lookit! I found a little pink daisy. Can I dig up the whole plant? Lookit! Is this a crocus?"

I longed to sit right down and admire each and every offering and hear just what was going to be done with it, but I couldn't. I simply couldn't leave Susan to cope with the thundering herd all alone.

We came back into the gameroom to find Susan grinning like a triumphant Brownie. "Guess what!" she said. "Mrs. Bean just called. She's been in touch with every single Brownie mother. Mr. Bean is picking up the popcorn when he picks up Phyllis. They are having a mothers' meeting at Patty's house for the purpose of stringing popcorn. She asked me if we wanted to come, but I told her we were *much* too busy."

"I think I'd like to go—" I began.

Susan interrupted. "Don't. I know what you have in

mind. More leaders. Wait until after Christmas. No mother in her right mind would volunteer at this time and you know it. Besides, they won't be able to cuss and discuss us, which is their prime object in going to the meeting. Anyway," she nodded toward the third grade table, "we have a little repair work to do on some of these presents and we'll have to do it tonight—Santa's gnomes mustn't be suspected."

I sighed and walked around the third grade table. "Could you help me finish this, huh?—Could you fix my terrarium?—Could you cut me a star? Could you fix my bulb?" No, I didn't have time to go to a mothers' meeting.

The next afternoon I had just finished mounds of spritz cookie dough and was cutting out a batch when the children came in from school trailing several Brownies. They demanded cookies, but I told them they weren't baked yet and I'd bring a plate down to the gameroom when they were ready.

Gloria glanced at my wiggley-legged camels and crooked stars and shook her head. "Want me to help you? I help Mother all the time. Are you going to decorate these? I know how to use a pastry tube and everything. Here, let me do that for you." In a businesslike manner she began to cut out reindeer which were so perfect they appeared to be cut out of paper. She slid them off the board with a spatula, slipped them onto the cookie sheet and said, "How many reindeer do you need?"

I shook my head. "I can't tell until I begin to pack them."

"Well, how many have you got?"

I pointed toward the row of canisters standing on the shelves under the windows. She lifted up each lid. "Brownies, datebars, pecan rolls, um-hum, you can't put spritz in round tins, they have to be kept flat or they'll break, um-hum. Well, I'll cut a couple of more sheets of reindeer and then switch to stars."

Gloria's prowess proved to be more fascinating than

Emily's wreaths or the Girl Scout ornaments, and the kitchen table was soon surrounded by helpers.

"Have you got your decorations?" Gloria asked.

I handed her the box of colored grit, the silver toothbreakers, and the bowl of icing.

"Have you got your food coloring for the icing?" Gloria asked. "Hand me a muffin tin. Have you got some paint brushes? Mari, go get me some from the gameroom."

She put a blob of icing in each section of the muffin pan, colored it, and set the Brownies to work.

We were still decorating when Jim came home. He ate a couple of samples, pronounced them delicious but not quite as crisp as last year, and then sat right down to help. His designs showed such originality and daring that even Gloria said, "Gee, Doctor Jay, you're sure good at painting. You ought to be a baker!"

I went downstairs to tell the wreath and ornament makers that it was five-thirty. Emily said, "Oh didn't I tell you? We brought our nosebags. We're going to work right through."

I came back and murmured this new facet to Jim who said, "What's a nosebag, lunch? Say! That's an idea." He held up a camel glittering with toothbreakers. "Why don't you Brownies call up your mothers and ask them if you can stay here for dinner? I'll drive you home at eight o'clock."

So while the artists painted angels with golden halos and blue wings, I baked cookies and changed our menu from creamed leftovers to creamed tunafish and noodles, which I was more than willing to do, because I was pretty sick of decorating cookies which were gulped and gone before I could say, "Merry—" let alone "Christmas."

The Girl Scouts and Brownies were called for by their parents at eight o'clock, but not the Seniors. They were waiting for their dates and couldn't leave until identical hoarse-voiced, large-footed gentlemen called for them.

Each time the doorbell rang, our daughters peered over the banisters and called, "Hi, Micky. Hi, Pete. Hi, Stan. Hi, Dave."

"How can they tell them apart?" Jim asked.

"They've been making wreaths for quite a spell," I answered.

The enormous, sweatered gentlemen cantered down into the gameroom, the Christmas carols changed to jive, and the whole house shook.

That was when we took to locking ourselves in the bedroom.

At breakfast Mari breathed, "Do you think Emily likes Micky? Do you think Judy'll go steady with Pete? Jody used to go steady with Stan, but he's going steady with Peachy, so she's going with Dave—"

"How on earth—" Jim's eyes widened.

"Wreathmaking's mighty instructive," I said. "Remember, only six more years—"

Jim grumbled, "Silliest thing I ever heard of. Little girls talking about going steady. If that's what the Girl Scouts teach them—"

"I'm not little," Mari said, "I'm almost ten years old."

The following Thursday afternoon Jim came home early, partially to keep tab on what was going on in his home, and partially to prepare for Christmas by getting his steelhead tackle in order. He came into the gameroom where I was boxing cookies, while Emily and the Seniors were making ornaments and entertaining Diana and Jane and Phyllis and our girls with tales of the "neat" house party they'd had over the week end. Fifteen Seniors with their Leaders and twenty "men" had gone over to the Brownie Camp to shingle the roofs and had danced and cooked outdoors and finished every single roof, and Judy'd almost broken up with Pete because Skippy bird-dogged her, and Jody'd danced with Stan, which made Peachy—

Jim growled and retired to his workshop, but he kept roaring, "Mary? Where's my—" until I felt it incumbent upon me to be a wife instead of a Leader and leave Emily's fascinating saga.

Diana, as was her custom on the odd occasions when she did decide to appear, had been sitting beside me absent-mindedly eating cookies, reading up on the boll weevil, and telling me occasional facts which she thought my feeble brain might encompass. The moment I got up to leave, she followed me, still saying in her soft voice, "—it feeds on the silky fibers *inside* the seed pods—"

I opened the door of the workroom to hear Jim hiss, "Moths! In my steelhead flies!"

"Moths? Flies?" Diana brightened.

"Lord yes. You'll have to tie some right away," Jim said.

"Right now?" I asked.

"Sure. You forget, we're going steelheading next week."

I hadn't forgotten, I'd been hoping every day that he'd forget. Not that I don't love steelheading, I do, more than any other kind of fishing, it was just that—I got out the fly tying equipment and the vise, set up a bridge table in the cranberry corner and prepared to be diverted by "he said" and "she said" while I tied the flies.

Diana, still following me, picked up Jim's fly box, looked the flies all over and said, "These are pretty good reproductions except they have the wrong colored wings and their bodies are not bright like this—"

I reached for the box. "Right or wrong, they're Doctor Jay's pet flies, and he'll have a conniption fit if you touch them."

Diana moved back just out of my reach and continued to pick up each fly and criticize it while I took out a #1 short-shanked hook, affixed the hackle fibers to the head and wound the flat silver body with several turns below the tail to form a tag. I was trying to copy a Parmachene Belle, but as manual dexterity is not my long suit, I was having my usual struggle.

"I can't do this now—" I muttered.

"I can," Diana said.

"I'm afraid it's too difficult for you, Diana, and for me too."

Diana ignored the foolish vaporings of an adult whenever a bug was involved. She merely picked up the other vise, affixed it to the table and began to tie the fly. She produced a perfect Parmachene Belle while I was still gritting my teeth and trying to wind the body.

"I like to do this," she picked up another hook. "Now which one shall I make?" She peered at the illustrations, and I told her to make any one she admired.

Of course she chose the brilliant Royal Coachman, a Jungle Cock fly which is so intricate I wouldn't even attempt it. Her slim fingers, and knowledge of bugs, enabled her to turn one out in nothing flat. "I'm not going to make Christmas presents, I'm going to tie flies," she remarked and picked up another hook.

One by one the Brownies came over to see what we were doing, and I literally shook with terror as they pounced on the equipment, rooted through the feathers, made mustaches out of the polar bear hair, and fought over the spools of metallic thread. Diana looked up and said in a voice just as cold and dictatorial as Katie's, "Put those down!" They dropped them. "Can't you see they're delicate? This is a Jungle Cock and this is muskrat fur and this is pheasant breast—"

"How did you know?" I looked up to see Jim standing over us.

I squeaked, "Look! Diana made a Royal Coachman!"

"So she did!" Jim examined Diana's Royal Coachman. "—and a darned good one. Where did you learn to do this, Diana?"

Diana was looking at the illustration, so she didn't bother

to answer. She continued reading softly, "—scarlet hackle fibers, white bucktail wing, Jungle Cock shoulders and a Peacock herl—what's a herl?" She looked up at Jim.

Whereat he settled right down in the Leader's chair and was immediately joined by Phyllis, and Jane and Mari and Sally and Heidi and her cat. I watched with fear and trembling while he took our precious polar bear hair to help Heidi tie a streamer fly. "This one will catch you a big fat salmon, Heidi." Not once was he impatient when they got bored and reverted to being silly, nor did he wince when Heidi tired of tying flies, took a clump of polar bear hair and tied it to a string so Cotton could jump at it.

I left them still tying flies and went upstairs to cook dinner.

That night at dinner, it was Jim's turn to brag. That Diana was a genius. She could tie two flies to his one, and she would have gone right on tying them, had they not run out of Jungle Cock. During Christmas vacation he was going to take Diana and the girls down to the tackle shop and let them buy whatever their little hearts desired in the way of feathers, fur and golden thread.

Heidi, a little bitter because Daddy liked Diana's flies best, said, "I suppose you aren't even going to tell Mother that Diana broke that little wingy thing off her vise—"

Jim waved that one away. "Who wants to go fishing during Christmas vacation?"

"I do, I do, I do, I do," we chorused.

As a result of Jim's Leadership, Diana came home with the girls four days running. We tied Jim the fanciest box of steelhead flies he'd ever seen, wrapped it up in paper on which Diana had painted flies of every description, and wrote on the card:

> To Jim, the new Brownie Leader,
> From an old Brownie Leader
> and DIANA

When we had finished and had put it on the top shelf of the Christmas closet, Diana said, "I'm going. Can I borrow this Fly-Tying book? I liked making that present. It's the first one I ever made," gathered up her felt bag, her books and her net and wandered out the door, not to appear again until January.

When I called Diana's mother to find out why she did not come to the Brownie meeting, a soft voice, very like Diana's, said, "What meeting? Oh—she didn't want to I guess. She's making insect reproductions. It was kind of you to show her how—" The soft voice trailed off and there was a click.

There was one wailing shepherd's flute which wound eerily through the gaiety of our holiday preparations. "Why-y-y-y-y?" from our Troop Treasurer, Jane.

If I said, "I can't find anything but blue and pink yarn, I guess we'll have to buy a ball of red," Jane wailed, "Why-y-y-y? Can't we use something we've already got?"

Every time we requested ten cents for glue, or twenty cents for luminous paint, or thirty-five cents for a roll of red shelf paper to wrap our presents in, Jane wailed, "Why-y-y-y? Do we have to use our Troop funds?"

"Maybe Jane wouldn't feel so badly if you took her with you when you went to buy the equipment," Susan said. "Explain to her that this isn't *her* money, it belongs to the whole Troop."

I explained all the way to the Ten Cent Store, where Mrs. White's heart was so wrung by Jane's woebegone face that she *gave* us a ball of red yarn. I explained all the way back, to no avail. As we got to the front door she said, "But if we spend our Troop funds, we won't have any and then we can't go to the bank."

Susan took Jane to the bank and came back shaking with laughter. "Do you remember that old story about the Indian who asked the banker how many horses you got? You should have seen Jane. She made the Teller show her just where the money was going, asked him how he could tell it from all the other money, and finished with, 'How do I know you'll give it back?' The thing that finally clinched it was the Teller's explanation that he was going to pay Jane to allow him to keep the Troop funds. Her whole face wreathed in smiles when she found out about interest."

The night Jim and Charlie took us to the fire station to show us the Christmas boxes, Susan and I offered to crawl all the way home, we were so ashamed. Mrs. Bean had three hundred boxes all labeled and ready for delivery by the various boys who were working their way toward a hot rod by driving for Murph.

Via the various agencies, she had combed the district and found every house where there was real need. These were no casual baskets for the poor; these were thoughtfully prepared, gaily wrapped Christmas presents. Each family got a Christmas dinner, a turkey provided by Dave, the butcher, at cost, stuffing and cranberry jelly and canned goods and apples and nuts and candy, provided by Vi and Murph. Shiny shoes, and clean pressed coats, and new caps and mittens, and dolls and wagons and tricycles and bicycles and trains and blocks and doll buggies. The firemen stood around proudly showing us each and every item. "I tell you, they can't say we don't take care of our own at Christmas," they said. "Santa Claus is sure coming down our chimneys."

Jim and Charlie stopped at the drugstore on the way home and bought each and every Brownie a new double box of crayons, round pointing scissors and a pencil box, as their contribution, and we all stayed up until one o'clock making each and every Brownie a candy wreath of her very own to take home with her.

"When I think of what I said about Mrs. Bean," I mourned.

"Don't think. String candy," Susan said, "we have to get twenty-three of these made by December twenty-third."

December twenty-third was the night the big fir down by the pond was going to be lighted for the first time. Everybody in the neighborhood was going to gather around it to sing Christmas carols. The Girl Scouts and the Brownies were to arrive fifteen minutes early, so they could form in Troops under the biggest lighted Christmas tree in the whole U-nited States!

Susan and Charlie and Peggy came over for supper so we could get the children fed and into their uniforms and down to the pond by seven forty-five. Jim had just said for the tenth time, "No, it isn't time yet. Now finish your dinner—" when the front door burst open and Phyllis came stalking into the dining room and handed Heidi a package. "This is for you. You can open it now 'cause it's my old one. Even if you aren't a Brownie, you have to know what to do. I have to hurry. Mymother's waiting in the car—"

Heidi tore off the wrappings. "Boy oh boy! A Brownie Handbook of my very own!" She beamed at Phyllis and then her eyes narrowed. "But I still might not be a Brownie—"

"But, honey—" Mari began and stopped as Phyllis shook her head.

Jim said, "Phyllis, that is the most thoughtful present—"

Phyllis drew herself up and saluted. "A Girl Scout is a friend to all—" A horn tooted impatiently and she turned and stalked out the door.

As we walked down to the Park, the children babbling with excitement in front of us, I had my old childish longing for a snowy Christmas. It was brisk and cold, but everything was so everlastingly green—

Promptly at eight o'clock, the tall fir tree which had been standing guard over the little pond for more than three hundred years burst into light. It shone down on serried rows of neighbors and the upturned faces of their children as we all sang, Silent Night, Holy Night.

Jim slipped his arm around me and murmured, "Look at their faces. Good, kindly, neighbors—" There was a long drawn out "Oh-oh-oh" of pure ecstacy from the children. It was snowing!

9

WHO AM I?

*D*URING Christmas vacation many of the Brownies, instead of being forced to wait until after school to visit us, were free to arrive early in the morning and stay until Daddy and Mommy picked them up at night on the way home from work. After spending ten days switching rapidly from wife to mother to mentor to Leader to psychologist and back again, I felt I had earned a brand new proficiency badge— Referee-First Class.

It began with Heidi's Christmas presents.

Being a little leery of Jim's reaction to Heidi's Santa Claus letter wherein she requested two rabbits, two hamsters, a new puppy and two new kitties, I had waited until the day *after* the Community Christmas tree to show it to him. He read it, smiled fondly and shook his head. "Oh no, Johnnie and his rabbits are unknowns. If we get two of Johnnie's rabbits, the first thing you know, we'll have more rabbits than children around this house, and that, my weak-minded mate, is a fate I do not care to contemplate."

He did, however, offer to consult good old Joe, the man who supplies the experimental animals for the Medical School.

The day before Christmas, Jim came home at three o'clock. "Come on. Let's drive out and see Joe."

Of course we came home with two BOY rabbits. "Oh, Jim! These are angora and they have pink ears!"—and two GIRL guinea pigs. "Oh, Jim! These are South American and they have long golden hair!"

Good old Joe, who was also an old friend of Heidi's, threw in two fancy animal cages with pans under the floor so it would be easy for *me* to keep the cages clean, and a couple of boxes of food, one for guinea pigs and one for rabbits, so it would be easy for *me* to feed Heidi's presents.

Jim, who is almost as weak-minded as I am where his young are concerned, was all for adding two hamsters. There, I balked. We'd had hamsters, remember? Gretchen's hamsters, in case he'd forgotten, could burrow through steel walls. "Remember the night we hunted hamsters until one o'clock in the morning and finally located them under the cushions on the couch?" I asked.

Jim remembered, but he just couldn't bear to disappoint Heidi. After all, this was probably the last year she'd believe in Santa Claus.

After the children were safely tucked in bed, we rescued the guinea pigs and rabbits from the back of the car and sneaked them down into the basement where we hoped they would remain until Santa Claus put them under the Christmas tree.

Jim stood looking down at the cages, a reminiscent smile playing around the corners of his mouth. "I'll bet the Brownies will get a kick out of these. When I was their age, I would have given anything I owned for a pet."

"Didn't you have any pets?" I asked.

He shrugged. "Mother didn't like animals."

Then, and not until then, did I remember Susan's antipathy toward animals of any kind.

After Susan's first Brownie meeting, she had said, "Do you

mind if the dogs don't come to the meetings? I'm sorry but I have a regular thing about animals." I had tried to be considerate, but the dogs continued to sneak into the meetings with Heidi.

The Brownies, sensing Susan's fear, had carried on a determined campaign to teach Mrs. Blake to know and love animals. "Aw come on, Mrs. Blake. Just hold this dear little caterpillar. He's so sweet and fuzzy—"

"He's fuzzy all right—" Susan had backed away and I had held the dear little caterpillar.

She had tried to admire our grasshopper and his endearing characteristic of spitting tobacco juice, but she had complained bitterly to me. "How can you stand to touch him? He's just like a dreadful little dried up old man!" Even when Hoppy was dead as a doornail but still a beloved part of our "insect collection" Susan had gone out of her way to avoid that shelf on the bookcase. "How do I know they're dead? Anyway, they give me the creeps."

Even the goldfish, surely the dullest and most inoffensive of pets, were actually repellant to Susan. The day Heidi brought them down to a meeting, one of them obligingly died. The Brownies were all for preserving him for their collection, but Susan fished him out of the bowl with a strainer and callously flushed him down the toilet, saying, "One down and two to go. Ugh!"

The day Gretchen's mother unselfishly loaned our Troop Gretchen's hamsters to keep as long as we wanted to, Susan had taken one look at them and whispered through set teeth, "Mary! I warn you. If they bring one of those ghastly little things near me, I'll scream!" I had seen to it that Gretchen's hamsters were kept at a safe distance, but even I could not prevent the Brownies from wearing them as if they were lapels.

Just what Susan would do when she discovered that we

had deliberately gone out and *bought* guinea pigs and rabbits—

Jim took my arm. "Come on, Mrs. Claus, we still have the stockings to fill, the presents to put under the tree and the sleighbells to ring."

Christmas morning Jim lit the living room fire, and I served hot cocoa while the girls crouched around the blaze chattering with excitement and opening their stockings. Mari's and Sally's stockings contained one hundred per cent Brownie accessories—flashlights, compasses and knives which caused cries of delight. Heidi's stocking contained the usual assortment of chocolate-flavored dog bones, a catnip mouse, parakeet ladder, turtle food, goldfish food, guinea pig food, and rabbit food. In the toe was a note from jolly old Saint Jay:

Dear Heidi:
You already have two dogs and one cat and one bird and two turtles and three goldfish, and you can borrow Gretchen's hamsters. I have given all my puppies and kittens to poor little girls who don't have any animals. Look under the Christmas tree.

Love,
Santa Claus

The girls made a rush for the Christmas tree, and amid shrieks of joy over the presents, Heidi was heard to exclaim, "Santy Claus made a mistake. These aren't Johnnie's rabbits. His are brown!"

The guinea pigs were such a squealing success (they never stopped squealing night or day) that even Mari said, "Aren't they darling, Mommy?" and invited Heidi to have a special animal exhibit for the first Troop meeting in January.

Sally crooned over her new baby doll and doll buggy and Mari switched around in her new sweater and skirt, but her favorite present by far was her new Girl Scout Handbook. "Now I can practice earning my proficiency badges. Phyllis has been practicing for a long time." Mari retired to a corner to read up on how to beat Phyllis.

Christmas afternoon, Susan and Charlie and Peggy dropped in for an eggnog and to bid us good-bye; they were going to Canada to look over the fishing possibilities. Susan took one look at Heidi's placidly chewing Christmas presents and shuddered. "What are you trying to do, Mary? Get rid of your assistant Leader?"

No, I was helping the Brownies dispose of her idiotic antipathy toward animals.

Meanwhile Peggy was muttering to Sally that she couldn't even play with *her* Christmas presents. *Her* mother and daddy were taking her to that darn old Canada.

Sally instantly clamored to have Peggy stay with us so they could play with their dolls.

Jim said why not, we all begged and pleaded, they protested faintly, and then went home to get Peggy's Christmas presents and her suitcase.

As they were leaving, Susan said, "You really are a lamb to take Peggy. I know she'll have much more fun than she would trailing around after us, and I must confess that I don't feel as badly as I should about imposing on you because you deliberately went out and bought guinea pigs and rabbits." She gave Peggy one last hug. "Now remember, you be a good girl and we'll be back New Year's night."

Peggy said, "Okay, okay, have a good time," and ran back to play with her Christmas presents.

Beginning the morning after Christmas, Phyllis, Gloria, Katie, Minnie, Jane, Durdey, Colleen, Patty and Betty arrived while Jim was finishing his breakfast. They stood around the table staring hungrily at him until, in self-defense, he produced toast and jam all around.

As he was leaving he said, "Can't a man even finish his breakfast in peace?" I reminded him that their mothers worked and they didn't have any place else to go. He shook his head, kissed me, and said, "Hamper, hamper, hamper—" and left.

The moment the door closed, the Brownies bounced up and down chanting, "What can we do to help you? Shall we do the dishes? Shall we make the beds? Shall we help clean up the house so you can play with us quicker?"

I was exceedingly grateful for so many eager errand runners, dishwashers, dusters and bedmakers, but a little dismayed when the housework was all done, it was still only ten o'clock, and I was again surrounded by eager "What'll-we-doers."

It wouldn't have been quite so bad if they had been able to play outdoors and work off some of their energy, but as it continued to rain drearily night and day, the yard was like a soggy wet sponge. Nor would it have been quite so distracting had not Gloria and Katie and Minnie and Jane and Colleen received Girl Scout Handbooks and also been determined to practice earning their badges in order to beat Phyllis.

The house echoed with "Mrs. Jay? Could you help us make an original design and use it in basketry—pottery—woodcarving—weaving—textile work—needlecraft—leather—metal?"

Not having the remotest idea how to do any of these things, I said we'd—ah—wait until the regular Brownie meetings to practice those crafts. Why not make notebooks and scrapbooks?

"We've already made notebooks and scrapbooks."

Were their Brownie plays okay for Literature and Dramatics, or should they make up special plays and read special books?

Oh no—their regular books and plays were just dandy.

Could I find a Symphony record for them so they could recognize two instruments? Did I know all the instruments?

Well—sometimes I could recognize some of them.

They already knew about getting acquainted with some-one from another country, because Katie was from Germany and Cherie was from France and Sumiko was from Japan. Should they call up Cherie and Sumiko and ask them to come over so they could find out some more?

I didn't think that was necessary. They could talk to Cherie and Sumiko when they went back to school.

Well then, would I help them learn the other countries' uniforms, pins, and Laws and tell them what Girl Guides did?

All day long I sidestepped proficiencies, muttering, "I wish to *heaven* I'd been a Girl Scout," and sneaking their Handbooks to see what fiendish request was in the offing.

They also carried around with them the smoldering punk of Sweet Reason which they blew on until it glowed and then used it to ignite quarrels with the younger children.

"You don't mind if we take full charge of your animals, do you, Honey?" they asked Heidi. Heidi and Betty didn't care to hand over their animals for the learning of Agriculture. Heidi shrieked, "You let our animals alone! Mo-ther-r-r!"

Nor did I care to have them take full charge of my house plants. "But Mrs. Jay, we have to do *something* to practice Agriculture." I would help them plant a seed or a bulb or root a cutting, but *not* while it was raining cats and dogs. Some other time—

Durdey and Sally and Peggy were perfectly content to spend all day in their cave under the piano playing with their new dolls. That is, they would have been content, had the practicers let them alone and not demanded their dolls to practice First Aid. Then, they fought and kicked and screamed like seagulls. "We don't *want* to practice caring for the injured. We want to play house. Mo-ther-r-r!"

"Mo-ther-r-r!" rang through the house like a siren while I ran from room to room putting out the little fires of Sweet Reason.

Each night I took the Leader's Guide to bed with me and studied it to see if there was anything I knew how to do which came under the head of a future badge. This research did not increase my skills or competence, but it did lead to some pretty uncomfortable soul searching.

Susan and I were managing to keep a large group of children fairly well amused one afternoon a week, but were we helping each individual child find herself and grow into a well-rounded person? Had the older girls become less dictatorial as a result of our Leadership, or was Sweet Reason just a natural growth process? Wouldn't it be much easier to predict the behavior of a child if, as the Leader's Guide reiterated, we knew her mother? True, most of the mothers worked, but wouldn't I be even more interested in my children's activities away from home if I could only be with them on week ends? When you came right down to it, was it possible to give twenty children ranging in age from seven to ten years old, intelligent, constructive Leadership?

The Leader's Guide writers said not, and they ought to know. They'd been handling Brownie Troops since 1918. They insisted that a Troop should consist of eight to sixteen girls of approximately the same age. Certainly the diversity in age was our major problem.

Susan was an inspired and experienced playground instructor, but this wasn't a playground, this was a Brownie Troop, and we were supposed to be inculcating Scout ideals in each and every child. Honor, loyalty, usefulness, helpfulness, courtesy, kindness to animals, obedience, cheerfulness, thriftiness, clean-mindedness—

"—I have done those things which I ought not to have done and have left undone those things which I ought to have done—"

Each night I fell asleep determined to concentrate on one Brownie at a time until I knew everything it was possible to know about her.

By noon the next day I was shouting, "*Stop* fighting!" and praying I would be able to keep the various age groups separated long enough to prevent them from actually injuring one another before the vacation was over.

One afternoon I thought I had them all settled down. I retired to the den to wrestle with my Christmas bills. I was frantically robbing Peter to pay Paul when a vicious battle broke out. Shrieks, wails, slaps, and yells of "Mo-ther-r-r!" I rushed into the living room to find Mari slapping Heidi because she was using Mari's hairbrush to smooth the guinea pigs' long golden hair and Sally was wailing that Heidi wouldn't allow Sally and Durdey and Peggy to dress the guinea pigs in doll sweaters and ride them around in the doll carriages. This fracas had been joined by the badge practicers who were trying to listen to Beethoven's Fifth in order to learn to recognize two instruments. Beethoven was roaring, the guinea pigs were squealing, Heidi and Betty were shrieking, Durdey and Peggy and Sally were bawling and the practicers were screaming. I stamped over to the piano, banged on it and held up three fingers.

"How would you all like to play Who Am I?" I asked.

"Why?" Phyllis bellowed over the squeals, sobs and Beethoven's closing thunder.

"Well—it would help you with Literature and Dramatics and—with Our Community—and—"

"But Mo-ther-r-r. We want to dress up the guinea pigs—" Sally began. "You—can't—even—touch my—guinea pigs—" Heidi stormed.

Three fingers. "Now suppose you all keep still and listen while I tell you about Who Am I? and then you can decide whether or not you want to play."

The necessary deletions from the adult game made my explanation even more confusing than usual, but it did keep them quiet. The one who was It went out of the room and thought up a person whom we all knew, someone in Our

Community, or a movie star, or a TV actor, or a character in a book we'd all read. Then It came back into the room, said, "Who am I?" and without saying one word, acted like that person until someone guessed who it was. The audience was allowed to ask twenty questions to help them guess. If at the end of that time they hadn't guessed, It was It again.

Phyllis and Katie were staring mutinously at me, so I hastily added that of course Who Am I? was a fine way to practice earning badges.

"How?" Katie asked.

"I get it!" To my astonishment, Minnie jumped up. "I know one, let me be It!"

And Minnie, our quiet, earnest, overanxious Minnie, proved to be an inspired pantomimic! She came in and sat down in a chair and was driving. Suddenly she stiffened, motioned haughtily and then stepping out of the car, walked over to the back of another chair, leaned her arm on it and began an earnest conversation. She appeared to ask for something, glanced at it and shook her head. More earnest conversation. Then she took something out of her pocket and began to write. Minnie was such an uncomfortably good traffic policeman that I shuddered reminiscently.

The audience was sitting forward, biting their lips and swallowing, their eyes fixed on Minnie. "Go on, Minnie, go on!" Minnie held up her arm, looked carefully both ways, and began to shepherd invisible children across the street. "Go on, go on—" She sauntered along swinging a billy club and checking doors to see they were locked. "Are you a prowler car—are you a policeman—are you Mr. Kelly?" they asked.

Minnie nodded, giggling and sparkling. She started to sit down to allow someone else to have a turn, but they clamored, "Aw, go on, Minnie, go on—do another one!"

Minnie was Vi, leaning her stout arms on the counter, alternating confidences and howling out grocery prices. She was Murph, skipping up the ladders, lugging in enormous boxes, and kidding the customers. She was Haze working on her books and leaning out of her nest above the grocery store to warn about bills that were getting too high. She was the shoemaker, polishing shoes, tapping on heels, and hobbling back and forth complaining about arthritis. She was the druggist measuring out a prescription, handing candy to a small child, and selling lipstick to an indecisive female. But most important of all, she was Minnie, giggling, enjoying herself, and actually playing!

Eventually Phyllis, who was incapable of allowing anyone else to have the center of attention for long, said she had one. Minnie sat down still incandescent with joy, and Phyllis marched out of the room.

She returned and stood perfectly still blinking through her glasses. Suddenly she began to open and close her mouth and wave her arms up and down like a semaphore.

"Are you the train guard? Are you a teacher? Are you a preacher?"

Phyllis shook her head, raised her right arm above her head and brought it down in short chopping strokes.

No questions, nothing but wrinkled brows including mine.

Phyllis sighed and walked over and jerked Katie, then Mari, then Colleen to their feet, and then let them go. It was not until she sat down, held her finger to her temple and fell over dead that Minnie leaned forward. "Were you a President of the United States? Did you split rails and free the slaves? Were you Abraham Lincoln?"

Phyllis sniffed, "Of course. Who else?" and sat down.

The audience jeered. "Aw, you don't do it right. You can't act worth beans. You do it, Minnie, you're wonderful, you ought to be on TV—"

Minnie could hardly wait to be It, and all afternoon I sat on the couch taking up and letting down hems (a necessity rather than a proficiency) while Minnie acted innumerable roles in Who Am I? The game never seemed to pall, there was a minimum of fighting, and I even had to remind Heidi and Betty to feed the squealing guinea pigs.

The next afternoon they all gathered to watch Minnie, and I excused myself to go out and put the meat in the oven. Jane got up and followed me. While I took the roast out of the icebox, Jane amused herself by wandering around the kitchen asking the price of the appliances and shaking her head disapprovingly at each cost. "Gee! You sure spend a lot of money. Don't you even have a budget?" she asked.

I said yes, but most of our equipment had been purchased over a number of years, meanwhile wondering what kind of home training produced such a money-conscious ten-year-old.

She said, "I probably never will earn my Homemaking badge. My Mom never lets me cook. She's afraid I'd ruin it and waste it."

I looked down into Jane's worried brown eyes, large with the possibility of waste, thought, "Here's a golden opportunity to help Jane grow into a well-rounded person," and asked her if she'd like to cook dinner for me.

Jane backed away. "Oh no! I wouldn't dare! What if you had to throw away the stuff I cooked. My Mom says waste is inexcusable. Oh no thanks, I'd better not." She picked up the meat bill which was lying beside the rump roast. "Four dollars and a half! Gosh all fishhooks! I wouldn't dare cook $4.50!"

I smoothed her braids, said, "Oh yes, you would. Come on, try it. Cooking's easy and besides it's fun! Come on!"

Jane was quivering with that leashed enthusiasm she reserved for collecting Troop funds. "Could I? I mean do you think I'd better? I mean do you think you could eat what I cooked?"

I gentled and praised and encouraged until she gingerly placed the roast in the pan. We had just finished seasoning it and putting it in the oven when the other Homemakers came out to see what we were doing and began to clamor to practice cooking too. I promised that we'd take turns cooking dinner, but tonight was Jane's turn and they were to go back into the living room and stay until she had finished. They grumbled and complained, but they retired.

At first Jane kept repeating, "Oh my gosh! I'll bet I've ruined it." After a while she relaxed and became carried away with the joy of cooking. "Do you think I could make an apple pie? Apple pie's my Dad's favorite, it's mine too. Do you think I could really and truly make an apple pie?"

I got out the crust mix, showed her how to read the directions on the package and supervised the rolling out, slicing of apples and seasoning. She was proudly trimming the edges when the badge earners came back. Could they just sit and watch Jane cook?

By this time Jane was so sure of herself, she said, "Aw, let 'em watch. After all, they might as well learn how to make an apple pie."

Gloria said, "That edge sure looks messy. It's supposed to be crimped. My Mom wouldn't dare try to sell a pie that looked like that. Is this the first pie you ever made? Gosh, I've been making pies since I was knee-high to a grasshopper."

Jane's face fell. "Aw you have not—" Gloria bristled. "I have too—" "Aw your baker makes them"—"Aw he does not"—and the fight was on.

I stopped that quarrel by suggesting that Gloria read aloud the Homemaking section of her new Girl Scout Handbook. Reading aloud was not one of Gloria's aptitudes, and the necessity of going to the den to prove that "nutrition" was too a word and it did too mean food and they had too had that word in school, took the fighters out of the kitchen to continue their bickering in the den.

Jane stayed with me and after she had finished making all

the preparations for dinner, so proud she was nearly bursting, I asked her if she'd like to stay and have dinner with us so she could see what a remarkably good cook she was.

Again she backed off. "Oh no. I'd better not. My Mom says if I don't do my chores every single day without being reminded, I don't get any allowance." Her eyes widened at the ghastly thought of a week with no allowance. "My Mom says money is hard to come by and you have to earn every cent you get in this world."

Thinking that this female Benjamin Franklin might not be quite so rigid if she could see her daughter's glowing face when she took her very own apple pie out of the oven, I offered to call Jane's mother and give her a play by play description of Jane's prowess, and to suggest that Jane be allowed to do her chores after dinner.

Jane's mother was distinctly frosty. She supposed Jane could stay for dinner, although she'd already cooked Jane's chop, but she guessed she could put it in the icebox. I gave an enthusiastic description of Jane's cooking to which she replied that she didn't see how I had the patience to teach children to cook. She couldn't bear to have Jane under foot while she was cooking. She supposed it was because I was a Brownie Leader.

I began to see why Susan loathed all mothers.

Jane ate hugely of the roast beef, browned potatoes, peas, tossed green salad and her very first apple pie. She pushed her chair back, patted her stomach and beamed around the table. "I sure am a good cook. Aren't I a good cook though? That was the best dinner I ever tasted and I cooked every bit of it all by myself. And I didn't waste one single thing, did I, Mrs. Jay? Not one single thing!"

After Jim had driven Jane home and our children were in bed, I told Jim about Jane's mother and her frigid reaction to my attempts at being friendly.

Jim said, "I wouldn't worry about it. She was probably

tired and a little miffed because Jane comes over here and keeps talking about what a fine time she has." He rumpled my hair. "Be honest, how would you feel if Mari preferred to stay at Jane's house all the time?"

How would I feel? Well, I'd be hurt and on the defensive and probably much more abrupt than Jane's mother had been.

Jim continued, "I should think it might be tactful to ask the mothers of our daily visitors at least to drop in for tea some afternoon or better yet, invite them to visit a Brownie meeting and let them see what your fatal charm is."

I explained that one of my original bargains with Susan was that she was never to lay eyes on a mother.

"That seems a little stringent—"

"You can't really blame Susan. She had a hideous time with interfering mothers when she was a playground instructor—"

Jim patted me consolingly. "Oh well, they'll get over it. How about asking a couple of our friends to dinner during the vacation?"

We had six of our friends to dinner the next night, but we also had Colleen's fried chicken and Colleen's angel food cake because it was Colleen's turn to practice Homemaking.

While the dinner preparations were under way, I discovered that Colleen had three brothers and two sisters besides Durdey. "Boy! When I get married, I'm never going to have children. I'm so tired of taking care of babies! Mom always has a new baby and I always have to take care of it." Her blue eyes were rebellious. "You know what I wish? I wish our Troop was just kids from our room. Then I wouldn't even have to watch out for Durdey. 'Course she's my little sister and I like her and all that, but Gee, I'd sure like it better if she wasn't in my Troop. That's why I wanted to be a Brownie. No babies!"

Sally was pulling at my arm, "Mo-ther-r-r! Come here."

She stood on tiptoe and whispered to me. "Mari's mad at you. She set the table for your dinner party just the way you do and you haven't even noticed. She says you like those other girls better than you do her."

I dropped Colleen's family problem like a hot coal and rushed into the dining room to admire my own child. I exclaimed and praised, but Mari continued to switch around straightening a knife here and a fork there, muttering, "I'm the only one who knows how to set a table for a dinner party. A lot you care. I've known how ever since I was eight years old—"

I protested that I did too care. I was very proud of her and she was my right hand and I didn't know what I'd do without her.

Mari beamed and hugged me. "After vacation's over and you've taught all those other kids how to cook, can I cook dinner for Daddy all by myself? And you won't even come into the kitchen? Promise?"

I promised, thinking that I'd been so busy bringing the other children out that I'd almost pushed my own reserved eldest back into her shell. Mari moved a glass an eighth of an inch, sighed and bustled out into the kitchen to boss Colleen's fried chicken.

Colleen could not stay for dinner. She had to go home and help take care of all those babies.

The night it was Gloria's turn to cook, she said she'd like to eat with us, but she didn't care to cook dinner. She'd been around cooking ever since she was knee-high to a grasshopper and she was sick and tired of it. "Do you know what? My Mom even used to bring me to the bakery when I was a baby in a basket!" When Gloria grew up she was going to live in a hotel and eat all her meals in restaurants. She'd stayed in a hotel once and it was just neat. She'd just ordered her meals and the waiter brought 'em. She didn't even know where the kitchen was! She hoped she never did earn her Homemaking badge, that's what she hoped.

Katie didn't care to cook either. She was enamored of the automatic washer and dryer. Could she put some clothes in all by herself? She stuffed in a basket of clothes and stood in front of the whirling drum, a pleased smile on her face. "Just think! You don't have to do one single thing but watch! My mother is from the old country and she says they don't use machines." Katie said her mother made her wash and iron and cook and knit and sew and clean house, but it wasn't any fun doing it at home. No machines. Like practicing, she just loved to play the piano, but she sure hated to practice with her mother sitting right beside her saying, "*One*, two, three, *one*, two, three—"

"Would you like to play for me?" I asked.

"Sure, if you want me to."

Katie arranged herself on the piano stool, smoothed her skirt and began to play a Mozart sonata. It was easy to see why Katie's mother counted. Katie had no sense of rhythm, the sonata sounded like a barrel bouncing down stairs.

"Mother won't let me play the songs I make up. Would you like to hear one?" She sang, about a quarter tone off, in a high wiggly soprano about the wind in the trees and the whispering breeze accompanying herself with a loud, bangy bass and many trills in the right hand. I was shuddering, but the Brownies surrounded the piano. "Can you play Four in a Boat? Can you play The Wayfarer's Grace? Can you play When E'er You Make a Promise?" She not only could, but she did. She played constantly, and I found myself counting under my breath, stumbling, and trying by sheer force of will to give Katie some sense of rhythm. I even tried guile and suggested all sorts of games to get her away from the piano, but nothing was as fascinating to Katie as the playing of her own compositions. I'd succeeded in bringing Katie too far out, now the trick was to get her back in.

I found an unexpected ally in Patty who had spent most of the vacation curled up in the den reading. She stormed into the living room. "Katie! Either play something you know, or don't play at all! I'm so sick of your sappy voice and those ugly made-up tunes I could scream!"

Katie flounced. "Well, Mrs. Bookworm, I suppose you know how to play better than I do."

"If I didn't, I wouldn't play at all, that's a cinch!" Patty stamped back into the den.

Katie got up from the piano and banged down the lid. "My mother likes to hear me play anyway. From now on, I'm only going to play for my mother."

Yes, by the end of the vacation I felt I knew the fourth graders pretty well. The things they disliked and why, and I thought I had garnered a pretty fair running plan of their homes and what their parents demanded of them. But I really hadn't had a chance to know Durdey and Peggy and Betty, I was too busy keeping them from being scorched by Sweet Reason. In order to know each Brownie well, it was essential that we split our Troop into two sections as soon as possible. If Susan didn't like the idea of being assistant Leader to two Troops, she could take the older girls on Wednesday and I'd be her assistant Leader. While she prepared them for Intermediate Scouting, I'd take the younger girls on Monday and ask a series of mothers to help me.

But when she and Charlie came in New Year's night to get Peggy, there was such an hysterical reunion that I didn't have the heart to bring up Brownie problems. Peggy clutched Susan and gave her a breathless and garbled version of how the Brownies had done every single bit of my housework. Charlie gave Jim an equally garbled version of the fishing potentialities in Canada, and Susan stroked Peggy's hair and murmured, "Um-m-m I missed you. Um-m-m I'm glad to see you."

I watched Susan and Peggy and thought, "If I'd been

separated from mine for ten days, would I give one whoop
about Brownie plans? I would not. I'd look them all over
for dire consequences of my absence, while I half listened
to their adventures and drank in their shining eyes, pink
cheeks and general round deliciousness." Monday would be
soon enough.

10

ANIMAL, VEGETABLE OR MINERAL

*M*ONDAY afternoon, Susan walked into the game-room, took one look at the sucking, mewing, chewing, squealing, snoring, divebombing zoo Heidi had taken such pains to arrange, said, "I can't come in. Sorry," and retreated to the laundry room.

I followed her. "I'll get rid of them, Susan. Mari asked Heidi to have an animal exhibit for the first meeting, so the fourth graders could study Agriculture, but I didn't realize she was going to bring them all down—"

Susan said, "I seem to have a psychic block. I think it started when I was eight years old. I was sent to my uncle's farm while my mother was in the hospital. Nobody explained anything to me, and I was homesick and terrified. Everywhere I went an animal bawled or bellowed or hissed or chased me. One day my uncle, who was only trying to be kind, took me out to the barn to show me where milk comes from. I can still see that row of horns and hear that crunching. He began to milk, which I thought was disgusting, and suddenly squirted warm milk in my mouth! Ugh! I haven't touched milk from that day to this." She rubbed her hand across her forehead and sighed. "I'll make it, but just give me time."

While Susan was recovering, I explained to the Brownies that perhaps it would be kinder to put the animals back where they belonged so nothing would happen to them.

Several of the ten-year-olds who had not been daily visitors were walking around looking at Heidi's exhibit, making typical remarks. "I'm sure glad I got a Brownie sweater instead of old rabbits for Christmas. Gosh, who wants rabbits—" and "Gosh, those are funny looking. What are they, guinea pigs? Lookit their long hair!"

Heidi's eyes filled with tears, "I'm never going to be a Brownie. I just *hate* those girls—"

Instantly my antagonism toward the tactless ten-year-old swelled up and threatened to burst. In order to keep from saying something equally tactless, I suggested that the fourth grade practice Homemaking by putting the gameroom in perfect order for our meeting while the younger children helped Heidi remove the animals. I went into the laundry room to tell Susan the coast was clear and to ask her what she thought about dividing up the Troop.

She listened while I briefed her on my experiences during the vacation and the reasons why I felt I did not have enough proficiency to handle the complacent ten-year-old.

Susan grinned. "Peggy told me about the fighting. She seemed to resent Phyllis even more than usual." She chewed the inside of her cheek and looked up at the ceiling. "It might work at that. Actually I can hardly wait for Peggy to start earning her badges."

"And have her start using Sweet Reason?" I was incredulous.

Susan laughed. "Even Sweet Reason. I'll have to admit that I much prefer to work with the older girls. They're more attentive and besides that, they bring back memories of my own struggles to earn badges."

"Well, I don't," I said flatly. "I have the capacity and attention span of a Brownie, and probably always will have. They know it and sympathize with me. The fourth-graders thinly disguise their impatience with my lack of skills."

"One man's meat is another man's poison—" Susan chuckled. "Oh well, it's too late to do anything about splitting up the Troop today. Let's take a trek into the Out-of-Doors. It's not raining and it's actually almost warm."

Susan's suggestion was greeted with shouts of joy from the whole Troop. The ten-year-olds collected the equipment and dripped honey and rules all over the room while we were drawing our rough sketch map of the Park and discussing what route we were to take, a dangerous journey of ten short blocks downhill.

Susan seemed to take Sweet Reason in her stride, but it was all this Girl Scout could do to keep Clean in Thought, Word and Deed, as Phyllis, in a voice even more saccharine than Mari's, said, "Mrs. Jay? Aren't you forgetting something?" She took out the First Aid Kit and smiled pityingly at me. "A Girl Scout never goes in the Out-of-Doors without her First Aid Kit."

I gritted my teeth and retired to the heartwarming company of the Brownies, who were still young enough to think I had a grain of sense, and grimly started to pack up the graham crackers and powdered milk and cocoa. Katie followed me over to the Brownie table. "Mrs. Jay, aren't you forgetting something?" She put the sugar can in the pack and shook her head. "A Girl Scout checks her pack before she leaves."

January, for some weird reason best known to the weather man, is usually balmy, soft and almost warm in our part of the world. Purple and white crocuses dot the rock gardens, snowdrops nod from the grass, lavender bells hang from the early rhododendron, and the dark red stems of the flowering trees are beginning to show pink froth.

"It's sunny! It's warm! It's spring!" twittered the robins. The Brownies, too, hopped in mud puddles, picking up leaves and twigs. Susan strode ahead of the older girls, chanting rules for the Out-of-Doors, while I, feeling as if I were trying to keep peas on a knife, tried to "Look at the pretty flars!" and keep track of the younger girls.

The about-to-be Tenderfeet took turns carrying "the pack" and "the First Aid Kit" and the "map," while we Brownies carried bags of stale bread to feed the huge flock of mallard ducks waiting to greet us at the Park.

We had progressed about two blocks when we ran across Diana, squatting on the sidewalk, her books, bag and net scattered around her, while she examined a large, vicious looking black ant. I admired the ant, told her we were going down to the Park and asked her if she'd like to come with us.

She didn't bother to answer, picked up her things and fell into step beside me. "—is a male worker. It doesn't attain its full size until it leaves the pupa stage." I listened, interested and amused, while Diana told me the ant was omnivorous; its nest usually consisted of chambers excavated under stones or logs; that there were two or three thousand varieties of ants, but this was a carpenter ant, and, eight blocks' worth of fascinating attributes of the ant later, I thought, "If I stick with my Brownies long enough, I not only will be able to earn my badges, but I may never need to attend a lecture to improve my mind."

By this time we had arrived at the Park, an area on the Lakeshore encompassing about twenty acres. Along the shore there is a long playfield with an outdoor cooking area, benches and tables under the trees, dressing rooms and a Rest House. The Park also crosses the Boulevard and goes up the hill. The hillside has been left as it was originally, tall trees, a jungle of underbrush, crisscrossing trails, and an occasional lookout, but the effect to a Brownie is of an impenetrable forest.

After our exhausting ten-block hike, it was necessary to eat. While we Brownies tore around picking up sticks and bark and driftwood, the "Tenderfeet" built a fire in the covered cooking stove, a monstrous iron drum which consumes a cord of wood at a time without becoming even faintly warm. Eventually the Treat was pronounced ready, we pulled two picnic tables together and the hostesses of the day served graham crackers and a lukewarm concoction, gritty and revoltingly gray, known as "Campcocoa."

When Mari said, "Why aren't you drinking your Campcocoa? Girl Scouts do not waste food, Honey," I snarled, "Campcocoa does *not* taste better when it's drunk Out-of-Doors."

Mari looked startled, and Susan raised one eyebrow. "Honey, may I remind you that a Girl Scout is courteous." I drank my Campcocoa.

After we'd eaten, Susan led the older girls in an animated discussion of a Trail hike, Trail signs, and how to walk softly so they could get close to little animals, birds and insects, and we Brownies jumped from the table and began to toss dry bread to the voracious ducks. When the older girls practiced tracking by sneaking up on the ducks who were also sneaking up on them, we Brownies laughed so hard we rolled on the ground.

"Honey," Mari said, "don't you think you ought to stop being silly and learn these Trail signs? Girl Scouts obey orders, and Mrs. Blake's waiting for you to practice Trail signs."

Obediently I got up and called my Brownies, and we too made Trail signs and practiced identifying them. We also surreptitiously collected two new cocoons and four snail shells and a log with wormholes in it. We were supposed to be listening, but actually *they* were chasing the ducks until they flew in a quacking cloud into the Lake, while I listened to Susan with one ear and thought, "Why hamper a walk through the woods with so many rules? Why not allow them to enjoy themselves? Brownies are supposed to be a play group not a classroom." I was beginning to feel that I knew them all so well that I could pretty nearly tell what they were going to do next. Diana would sit by herself, examining her ant, until she happened to run across another insect. Minnie would find a flower where none had ever bloomed before. Durdey would sneak up and put sand down Sally's neck and then tattle when Sally put sand down *her* neck. Gretchen and Linda and Wendy would crumble their cookies and throw them up in the air calling, "Here Birdie, here Birdie," and then dissolve in a heap of helpless giggles. Susan's shy, retiring Peggy would blow cocoa on Betty and then quickly pour cocoa on the ground in a magic circle and yell, "Can't catch me-e-e, 'cause you can't catch a flea-ea-ea."

I was indulgently watching these predictions come true when Susan called, "Mary? Better get your group and come over and sit down at the tables. They've got to know the Trail signs, or we can't take them into the woods."

When everyone was seated (even Diana was present, although one could hardly say she was listening) Susan began. "We have set the Park as our boundary. No one is to go outside the Park. Understand?" They understood. "We will divide up into two Teams. Mrs. Jay will lead one Team and I will lead the other. Understand?" They understood. "We will use our Buddy system and will have one 'Tenderfoot' to every three Brownies. Understand?" They understood. "My team will set the Trail and make the signs nine feet apart. Don't forget to rub out the Trail signs as you follow, so we won't get mixed up the next time we take a forest hike. Everybody understand? Any questions?"

There were no questions. They understood.

"Remember. You are to have someone with you at all

times. You are never to leave the Trail for any reason. We'll go across the Boulevard and through the woods. The end of the Trail will be here at the Rest House."

We gave Susan and her group a twenty-minute head start. During that time I went over the sample Trail signs again to be sure the Brownies recognized and knew the meaning of each one. What does an arrow mean? Straight ahead. What does a big rock with a little rock on top and one to the left mean? Turn to the left. What does a big rock with a little rock on top and one to the right mean? Turn to the right. Three rocks piled up? Warning. Stop, look and listen. "Remember," I concluded, "if you aren't sure what to do, wait for me. I'll be at the end of our Team."

We started to separate into Buddies and immediately ran into trouble. Gretchen and Linda and Wendy couldn't be two Buddies, they had to be three Buddies. "What did Mrs. Blake tell you?" I asked. They looked up at the sky, and at one another, and shook their heads. Minnie sighed and looked responsible. "Girl Scouts obey orders. I'll go with them, Mrs. Jay."

We started across the field with Diana, never an orthodox Buddy, still sticking to me and talking about the ant. She stooped suddenly to lift up a rock, and I almost fell headlong over her. She saw ants on every leaf and twig which she felt called upon to gather and describe in infinite detail. I absent-mindedly answered, "They do! They are!" and kept my eyes alternately on the Trail signs and the Brownies. We started into the woods. Twig arrow, straight ahead. I kicked it aside. Rock on the left side, left, I obliterated it. Three rocks piled up—slippery bank. The tall trees threw lovely shadows on the Brownies' excited faces and their noses twitched with the smells of the forest and unpolluted earth. They disappeared around a bend in the trail and almost immediately I heard a shrill whistle, our Troop call for help. I ran ahead and the whistle came again, from the underbrush on the upper side of the trail.

I called over my shoulder, "Come on, Diana," and began to fight my way through the tall salal and huckleberry. Above me I saw Gretchen and Linda and Wendy hopelessly entangled in a mound of blackberry vines. Minnie was trying to pull the long strands away from them and in so doing, was ripping her arms with angry scratches.

As I began to free them from the wicked thorny strands, I asked why they weren't on the Trail following the signs. "We were," they chorused, "but the arrow said to crawl in here, so we did and got stuck."

Minnie shook her head. "No, that isn't what happened. They ran ahead of me and thought a wild blackberry vine was an arrow and when I caught up with them, they were already stuck."

Ten minutes, and a good scolding, later, they were disentangled, but it was necessary to spend some more time with the First Aid Kit repairing scratches.

When we got back to the Trail, there was no sign of Diana. Minnie said, "Come on. We have to catch up with the rest of our Team. Diana will be all right. Her father and mother let her come to the Park alone all she wants to. Come on."

I knew Minnie was scrupulously accurate and the most responsible child in the Troop. After all, we were in the Park and, although the underbrush was so high it was over their heads and paths crisscrossed in every direction, most of the children had played in our Park since they were old enough to walk. But they were not supposed to be left alone. It was hard to know whether I should catch up with the Team or stay behind and hunt Diana.

As this flashed through my mind, I said, "Minnie, could you take Gretchen and Linda and Wendy and follow the Team to Mrs. Blake while I hunt Diana?"

Minnie said, "Sure. I know every single trail in this Park."

"Remember, Minnie, you're almost a Tenderfoot, and Girl Scouts obey orders." I hoped my voice did not betray my anxiety. The shadows were beginning to lengthen. Across my mind flashed dire warnings in the newspapers. "Any group of small children is irresistibly attractive to psychopaths. Do not allow your children to go alone to theatres, zoos, or parks."

Minnie said, "Mrs. Jay? I think you ought to go with us. Let's run along the Trail just as fast as we can and get Mrs. Blake and the other Team and then we can come back and hunt Diana."

No Apaches ever picked out Trail signs faster than we did. We got to the Rest House and Susan just as her team was putting down the last Trail sign. I took Susan aside and whispered that we had lost Diana. Her eyes widened. "How did you do that?" I explained, Susan nodded and turned to the babbling Teams who were receiving the news from Minnie.

In a gay voice, Susan said, "Now we have a chance to backtrack our Trail and practice our Indian tracking. We have to find Diana. Mrs. Jay will lead you, and I'll be along in a minute. Find your Buddies and line up. Look both ways before you cross the Boulevard." While they were lining up, she murmured to me, "I'll run over to the store on the corner and call the Council and ask Pat Smith what to do. I don't want to call Mrs. Lamson and get her all worked up in case you run across Diana before I get back. Let them hunt, but don't let them leave the Trail. Keep warning them, but don't let them see you're frightened, or they'll panic. I'll be back just as fast as I can get here."

She started diagonally across the playfield after I shepherded the Brownies across the Boulevard and into the woods. When we reached the section of the Trail where we'd lost Diana, I thanked heaven that I'd been too upset to finish obliterating the Trail signs. There were the three rocks piled up, Danger! I said, "Now here's where Diana disappeared. We'll see who has the sharpest eyes. Keep calling her. Go up and down the Trails as far as the next Lookout. Come back after you've been down each Trail. Don't leave the Trails and don't run so fast you fall down. I'll stay right there at the Lookout so I can see you. Remember, you are Brownie Scouts. Girl Scouts obey orders." They bobbed up and down in front of me, like leashed puppies. The moment they were released, they darted down the Trails.

Katie and Colleen asked permission to go back to the cooking area and see if Diana had wandered down there. I knew I could see them below me, so I said yes, but to come right back when they'd covered the playfield and to be careful crossing the Boulevard.

As Katie and Colleen ran up and down the beach, I could hear faint calls, "Diana! Diana! Where are you hiding?" Suddenly I thought of the Lake. Could Diana swim? I tried to remember Mrs. Lamson's questionnaire. All I could recall was the comment, "I'm afraid Diana will never make a very good Brownie. She seems to be more interested in insects than in children of her own age."

The shadows were growing longer and longer and the sky was turning pink. From all around me on the trails came, "Diana! Diana! Where are you?"

What if we were still hunting when it got dark!

It seemed years, but it was probably half an hour later, when Susan came running up the trail. Behind her was Miss Dale! Susan murmured, "I called the Council. Pat Smith was out, and Miss Dale offered to drive out and help us."

Miss Dale said, "Don't worry. We'll find her."

The Brownies clustered around us saying excitedly, "Diana's sure got a good hiding place. We can't find her anywhere. We've called and called."

Miss Dale suggested that Susan round up the Brownies, take them down to the cooking area and play games with them while we scoured the woods for Diana.

When they were out of earshot, Miss Dale asked, "Is this where you saw Diana last?"

I nodded. "Within a radius of nine feet. Yes, here is the Danger sign. She was right beside me—"

"Always obliterate your trail signs," she said, casting around and around, looking to the right and left, her eyes missing nothing. Again she reminded me of a circling eagle. I must have muttered something about quoting rules at a time like this, because she looked up and fixed me with her cold, light gray eyes. "Rules prevent situations like this." She stooped. "This rock has been turned over," turned and started up the hill to the right of the Trail. "Stepped on a fern here—This bush has a broken branch—ground is soft— yes, here are footprints," on and on, Indian tracking, tricky at all times, but almost impossible in a public terrain.

I panted, "Do you think she would climb clear up here?"

"They'll go miles when they're interested. She was your Buddy, wasn't she? What was she talking about?"

"Ants," I said, "carpenter ants."

Miss Dale stopped and eyed the underbrush above us. "Logs!" She climbed rapidly toward the huge fanshaped root of a felled cedar. "Come on, she probably found an ant hill."

We ran along the top of the log, climbed over the root, and there, lying on her stomach, watching a line of carpenter ants, was Diana.

At the sight of her small absorbed figure, I almost burst out crying and wailed, "Diana! Why didn't you answer when we called?"

Diana pointed to a series of small holes in the log. "See? There are the galleries and there are—"

Miss Dale snapped, "Diana! A Brownie does not leave the

Trail for any reason. She never leaves her Buddy. You have left Mrs. Jay alone all afternoon. She has been worried and frightened. She might have been hurt or lost when she was calling you. Why didn't you answer?"

Diana stood up and fixed her enormous black eyes first on Miss Dale and then on me. "Were you lost, Mrs. Jay? I'm sorry, I thought you knew these woods. I come here all the time and I didn't think about you." She smiled, her melting, exquisite smile. "Here. I'll give you this worker ant for your own." She handed me her vicious ant and started down the Trail ahead of us, completely ignoring Miss Dale who was quoting Trail rules every step of the way.

The next afternoon Susan and I were having a cup of tea in the living room and discussing the prevention of potential Out-of-Doors catastrophes, while Katie and Phyllis and Patty and Colleen and Mari were Homemaking a batch of chocolate chip cookies in the kitchen, and Sally and Durdey and Peggy and Heidi and Betty were peacefully playing dolls with the guinea pigs under the piano.

Susan closed my Leader's Guide. "Actually I suppose we shouldn't have attempted forest trails with such a big Troop—"

"It isn't a question of the size of the Troop, Susan, it is the difference in ages. The fourth-graders would have been perfectly capable of taking that Trail, but Gretchen and Linda and Wendy and Diana—we really should have two meetings a week. We could use Charlie's idea and invite two mothers each week to help us—"

Susan shook her head. "Not while I have the strength to put my tongue to the back of my teeth. No mothers. Period."

"But Susan, why not?"

"Because, Honey, you're such a fanatic Friend to All that

in no time we'd have twenty mothers and heaven only knows how many Brown—" she stopped and I looked up.

Diana was walking slowly toward us carrying a Chinese bowl containing an exquisite gray branch from which hung suspended five large gray cocoons. She held it out to me. "I want to give you this because I left you alone when you were my Buddy. These are the giant swallowtail butterflies my father gave me for Christmas. One of them is going to hatch—"

She put the bowl down on the coffee table and knelt beside it, her eyes fixed on the top chrysalis. It was translucent and there was visible movement within it. As it began to split, Susan gave a faint moan and stood up.

I was transfixed as I watched a large butterfly, weak and damp, push its way into the air. It slowly crawled out on a twig, hung head down and gradually unfolded four-inch wings.

Susan made another slight sound, and I looked up to see her staring at the butterfly, her face as white as a sheet. I asked her if she was all right. She nodded.

Diana breathed, "Oh—you're so beautiful—" and reached out her first finger. The butterfly fanned more strongly. "My father said you would have velvety black wings and golden bars and dots, but I didn't know—" The butterfly stepped onto her outstretched finger, and she rose and moved with trancelike steps toward Susan. I started to move in front of Susan, but she shook her head imperceptibly, held out a shaking finger and allowed the butterfly to step onto her hand.

Diana's face lighted up. "Mrs. Blake! You like him!"

Susan's eyes filled with tears and her mouth trembled. "I wouldn't go that far, Diana, but I love you, and your butterfly is the most beautiful thing I have ever seen." She turned to me. "I too am capable of making a gracious gesture. Two meetings it is, but no mothers!"

11

LITTLE DROPS OF WATER—

$\mathcal{S}$USAN and I found that trying to strengthen a
Brownie Troop by splitting it in half in the middle of the
year was like trying to repair a leaky roof by putting little
pans of water under the drips. No sooner had we caught
one leak than we heard an ominous splat from another direction.

The first breach was the attitude of the Brownies. Being
mothers, we were prepared to have any sudden change in
routine greeted with suspicion, but we were unprepared for
floods of protest.

Monday after the hike, as soon as they had all settled
down, I got up and announced brightly that we were going
to start the New Year right, by dividing our Troop into two
Troops. The "Tenderfeet" of the near future would meet on
Wednesday afternoon, at which time Mrs. Blake would be
their Leader. The Brownies would continue to meet on
Monday afternoon and I would be their Leader.

This announcement was received with shocked silence,
their mouths making round "O's" of astonishment. Then
there arose a menacing rumble which soon grew into roars
of outrage.

"This is *our* Brownie Troop—We don't *want* two Troops—Who said you could make two Troops?—"

Older sisters rushed over and clutched little sisters. Colleen clung to Durdey who burst into tears and pointed her finger at me. "Sthe thayth sthe won't let me sthay with you-ou-ou—"

Colleen stuck out her lower lip and glared at me. "I *told* you I was supposed to take care of my little sister. I'm going to tell my Mom on you—"

"Yeah!" Patty clutched Betty. "She never even let me *play* with Betty during vacation."

Mari and Sally and Heidi said, "Mo-ther-r-r!"

I just stood there too stunned to speak.

Susan murmured, "Grateful little monsters, aren't they? Let me try." She stood up and raised three fingers. "How many of you fourth-graders could meet on Wednesday afternoon?"

Three hands flicked above the table and were instantly lowered. All faces glowered like thunderclouds.

"What about the rest of you?" Susan asked.

Orthodontist, tap dancing, ballet lesson, eye doctor, baton lesson, riding lesson, music lesson, everything under the sun seemed to be dedicated to Wednesday afternoon. Susan and I had had no idea the fourth graders' families were so prosperous.

"How many of you could change these appointments to another day?"

No hands were raised. Heads shook. Lips stuck out. Their mothers sure would be mad at us. Monday was Brownie Day, not Wednesday. They'd *always* had Brownies on Monday. Mrs. Burton never tried to divide up the Troop. "Why-y-y-y?"

It was a good question. Realizing that I could not very well explain that I wished to know each of these ungrateful little monsters better, I retreated to the Leader's Guide and said, "A Brownie Troop is only supposed to have sixteen members—"

Mutinous silence broken by Jane who said, "Well, I notice that two of the Brownies are your very own children and then there's Heidi—"

Susan hastily interposed. "We believe that you would enjoy being Brownies more if you were divided into two Troops. However, our decision isn't final. Suppose you talk it over among yourselves."

The younger children sat perfectly still looking scared and bereft. The "Tenderfeet" went to the opposite end of the gameroom and formed a football huddle from which came grumbles, protests and "Why-y-y-y-y?"

"I'm beginning to wonder 'why-y-y-y?' myself," Susan sighed.

Phyllis and Katie and Mari left the huddle and came stalking up to us, their nostrils flared and their mouths pursed. Phyllis saluted. "It is our thinking that we like our Troop just the way it is. We don't want two Troops and we don't want two meetings a week. A Brownie Scout is supposed to help other people and we like to help the younger children. We want to meet just like we always do, on Monday. All together."

The emissaries turned and marched back to their own table as the whole Troop shouted, "Yay-ay-ay-ay-ay!"

Susan shrugged. "Give them time. They'll get used to the idea. Watch this."

She walked over to the fourth-grade table, picked up Katie's Girl Scout Handbook, read it a moment and shook her head. "It would be fun, but of course we can't all do it—"

"What would be fun?"—"What do you mean?"—"Why can't we do it?"

She removed her intricately woven belt, held it across her hands and looked sadly at it. "Braided leather with a carved buckle. I made this belt when I was a Girl Scout. I remember I used a scriber, a skiving knife, a snap setter, an awl, a drive punch and a slit punch. Yes, I'll never forget the day I earned my leather proficiency badge by completing this belt."

"Lemme see! Lemme see—". Susan passed the belt around.

Meanwhile I'd been trying to lift the gloom at the third-grade table by distributing the carefully hoarded Walt Disney's True Life Adventures I had cut out of the paper. But my group was intent on listening to the tragic story of Susan's belt. They too began to clamor, "Lemme see! Lemme see!"

Susan passed the belt around our table. "I wanna make one, can I make one too?" Susan shook her head. "When I made this belt, I was a Girl Scout. I'd already finished doing every single thing my Brownie Leader could think of."

There was an actual whir in the air as mine whisked open their Handbooks to try to complete every single thing in one afternoon.

"Of course my Nature notebook was the first thing I completed—" Susan said thoughtfully.

Bang went the Handbooks, the Nature Notebooks were snapped open, and Walt Disney was pasted in so neatly it was untrue to life.

Above their bent heads, Susan made the 4-0 signal, picked up her belt and went back to the fourth-grade table.

"How do we start? What do we do?" they gabbled.

"The first thing I ever made in leather was a bookmark. First I found out all about leather, where it came from, how the hides were tanned, how it was softened. Then I drew an original design—"

There was no question about it, that was the quietest, most concentrated Brownie Troop meeting we ever had.

While they were putting on their coats, Susan patted my

shoulder. "It's simple. Just keep dropping water on their heads, and in no time at all they'll be begging for two Troops."

While I was cooking dinner, the telephone began to ring. Colleen's mother wanted to know if it was true that we were going to divide up the Troop and have two meetings a week. Yes, it was true. Sixteen was the maximum number a Leader could handle efficiently, and there was such a divergence in ages in our Troop we had decided to have two Troops. Pause. She was afraid that wouldn't do at all for Colleen and Durdey. Colleen couldn't come without Durdey, and of course Durdey couldn't come without Colleen. She thought I'd better leave the Brownie Troop just the way it was. Long explanation on my part as to why it was difficult to handle children of different ages in one Troop. Pause— "I'm sorry, but I just can't allow Colleen to come without Durdey." Well, perhaps Colleen and Durdey could both come on Mondays and Wednesdays. Colleen could play with Mari while Durdey was at her Troop meeting. Oh no, that was asking too much. She thought it would be much better if we just left the Troop the way it was. Mrs. Burton didn't seem to have any trouble. Pause. We'd let her know what we decided to do.

No sooner had I hung up than Patty's mother called. Was it true that Patty could no longer bring Betty to the Brownie meetings? No. Long explanation as to why we felt it necessary to divide up the Troop. "But I still don't see why. Patty says you have such a large room—" pause "Of course I've never seen it—" pause "I did want to thank you for having Patty and Betty at your house during vacation. I didn't realize they were so much trouble—" They weren't any trouble. Repetition of long explanation as to why we were splitting up the Troop. Pause. "I just know you would feel differently about this, Mrs. Jay, if you realized how close Patty and Betty have always been." Pause while I recalled that Patty had never spoken to Betty during vacation except to snarl, "Get *out* of here. Can't you see I'm reading? Now go on and play with Heidi or I'll tell Mom on you."

"—they've always seemed more like twins than sisters."

Nevertheless, we felt it essential to divide up the Troop and have two meetings a week. Perhaps if Patty and Betty both came on both days, they wouldn't be too crushed by the necessary two-hour separation.

"Well—if you're sure you don't mind—"

Then Gretchen's mother called. She and Linda's mother and Wendy's mother had been playing bridge when the children came home and they were *so* upset to hear we were going to break up the Brownie Troop. Gretchen and Linda and Wendy had enjoyed being Brownies *so* much. We were not breaking up the Troop, we were merely dividing up the Troop. I had just launched into the long explanation again when there were roars from our dining room. "Hurry *up*, Mother. Daddy's waiting to carve."

I hastily agreed that children were *so* funny, they never *did* get things straight and promised to let Gretchen's mother know when we split up the Troop.

As I slid into my seat at the table, Jim asked what all the fuss was about.

There wasn't any fuss. It was just that—long explanation as to why we were going to divide up the Troop.

"Do you mean to tell me you are going to have two Brownie meetings a week?"

Just until we found some more Leaders. There was no rush about it. Of course there would be a lot of extra telephoning. I'd have to call all the mothers and make arrangements for dental and dancing and doctor appointments to be changed—it wouldn't happen for a while yet.

Mari and Sally and Heidi had been conferring in low voices while Jim and I were talking.

Mari said, "I wouldn't do it if I were you, Mother. Phyllis

says you can't divide up a Brownie Troop. She says if you do, she's going down to the Council and tell Miss Smith and Miss Dale on you and she's going to tell her mother and Mrs. Lyons. Phyllis says we promised to help other people every day. We're *supposed* to help the little children—"

"I'm not little!" Sally fumed. "I'm almost eight and a half—"

Heidi interrupted, "Phyllis never helps me. Ever since she gave me her old Handbook, I'm just practically her slave."

"Heidi! A Girl Scout is loyal!" Mari said.

"I'm not a Girl Scout and if you don't keep still, I never will be."

Jim was frowning, and in order to restore a pleasant dinner atmosphere, I made a grave tactical error. I tried to reduce the long explanation to Brownie level, was interrupted constantly by "Who, who, why, why, what, what, where, where," and somehow managed to give the impression that we were dividing up the Troop to make room for more Brownies.

When *that* news leaked out, I was flooded with telephone calls. Was it true that we were going to have two Brownie Troops? Could we make room for Darleen, or Sandra, or Bettyjean, or Sally Sue, or Eloise?

No, we were sorry but our Troop was already overcrowded.

"But your Sally told Darleen (and Sandra, and Bettyjean, and Sally Sue, and Eloise) that you were going to take in more Brownies."

I jumped on Sally who wailed, "But Mo-ther-r-r. That's what you said—"

Susan called. "Have you been being a Friend to All again?"

No, I'd been spending all my waking hours repeating the long explanation as to why we were dividing up the Troop and repeating that we were *not* taking in any more Brownies.

"The dear mothers are certainly up in arms!"

"I'm beginning to see what you mean when you say, 'Mothers are the root of all evil.'"

Susan giggled. "Don't let them get you down, but don't give an inch."

More telephone calls. "*What* can I do? Darleen (or Sandra, or Bettyjean, or Sally Sue, or Eloise) keeps following me around asking, 'Why can't I be a Brownie?' What *can* I do?"

"You might try calling Mrs. Lyons, the neighborhood chairman, or the Council, or better yet, start a new Brownie Troop."

Oh-oh-oh-oh no-o-o-o. They couldn't possibly do that. They had younger children or previous commitments or they worked, but if we'd just take Darleen (or Sandra, or Bettyjean, or Sally Sue, or Eloise)—

As far as I knew, there was only one sure way to get a child into a Brownie Troop and that was to become a Brownie Leader yourself. Bang went the receiver.

Then Mrs. Lyons called. Was it true that there was now room in our Troop for more children? No, it was not true. Long explanation as to why we were dividing up the Troop. Several mothers had called her. Yes, they'd also called me. I'd told them to start new Troops. She did wish she could get more mothers interested in being Leaders. She'd tried and tried, but this was such a difficult district—

Sorry, but our Troop was full.

Then Pat Smith called. "What is this about dividing up your Troop so you can take in more members?" We hadn't even divided it yet, we'd merely suggested it. As a result the heavens had opened up. If and when we did divide it, we were not going to take more children but give ourselves a chance to concentrate on the ones we already had.

"Excellent. Is there anything I can do to help?"

I didn't think so. We'd come down to the Council and fill out the necessary forms as soon as we had everything under control.

At this point the weather man thought we'd had enough mild weather and released the pent-up rain in torrents. It poured so hard the rain splatted up from the pavements, and the gutters ran with muddy rivulets in which the Brownies ran all the way to the meetings. Splashing gaily down the outside entrance stairs, they came dripping into the laundry room where Susan and I lay in wait for them. We saw that they took off their soaking wet coats and hung them up on hangers suspended from the overhead pipes, took off their galoshes, poured the excess water in the laundry trays, and put them upside down to dry. We distributed paper towels to dry their faces, hands and hair and sent them in to get warm in front of the fire. True, the basement smelled like a Chinese laundry, but we didn't mind, we were so deeply grateful to the thoughtful Lumber Baron who had provided a basement with separate rooms and doors that could be shut.

While the Brownies were steaming in front of the fire, we doled out hot cocoa so they could stop shivering and start meeting. During this warm-up, we retired to our corner, got our Troop records and went over any little details which needed clearing up before we started to lead our respective Troops.

We were checking the Troop attendance sheet when we discovered three new steamy bodies, tense with expectation, stumbling over their names in their anxiety to please so they too could come in out of the rain. Unfortunately, their names were *not* Darleen, or Sandra, or Bettyjean, or Eloise. They were Marcy and Cindy and Kathe and were in the second grade.

Susan whipped around. "Have you been a Friend to All again?"

I shook my head.

"You're incorrigible and I'm incapable of turning away a soaking wet child. I warn you, if we let these stay, the mothers will be on us like a pack of wolves."

She walked over to the fourth-grade table and held a low-voiced conference. Turning to our group, she said, "Do you mind if we don't hold our formal meeting today? We'd like to go up to the kitchen to have our meeting. We feel that soaking leather is a little advanced for you girls." Winking at me, she led the leather-soakers, whose stomachs were sticking out with advancement, out of the room.

As the last one disappeared, her Peggy asked dispiritedly, "Now Mother's gone, what'll we do?"

I said that now we could do exactly as we liked. We'd get out our Brownie Handbooks and choose just what we wanted to do most.

Peggy said, "We can't do Out-of-Doors 'cause it's raining." More gloomy silence while they read their Handbooks. "It says here, 'You may elect a chairman, a secretary or scribe, and a treasurer.' Is a chairman the same as a president?" Peggy asked.

Yes, exactly the same thing.

Peggy leaned forward, licking her lips. "Could we have our own election and choose our own president?"

They certainly could. When you had your very own Brownie Troop, you could do all sorts of things.

The sun broke through the clouds. Faces were radiant. Boy, oh boy! This was living! Giving a perfect imitation of Jane's quivering enthusiasm, my own gentle Sally snapped, "I'm treasurer. I've watched Jane. I know how. There's nine of us, not counting Heidi—"

"You never count me," Heidi growled.

"—that's forty-five cents. Everybody bring their dues?"

Peggy sneered, "Take it easy, Greasy, you aren't elected yet."

Sally's face fell, but she cheered up again when the votes were counted. Peggy was elected president, Durdey secretary, and Sally treasurer.

Heidi went over and threw herself down in front of the fireplace between Dagmar and Spot, muttering, "Now Peggy's going to act just like Phyllis."

This wasn't strictly true. Peggy was a trifle less abrupt than Phyllis, probably because she had not been raised by permissive techniques and had a faint glimmering of the rights of others. Nor was Sally quite as money mad as Jane, probably because she received her weekly allowance even if she did forget to make her bed once or twice, but Durdey proved to be far more irritating than Patty, not because she was withdrawn and read all the time but because she was Durdey. Exquisite, dimpled, a halo of black curls, melting Irish blue eyes, which could harden into blue glass when she didn't wish to cooperate.

"You *have* to write down the minutes," Peggy implored.

"I don't want to write down the minuteth. My dolly doethn't want me to, do you, Dolly?" Durdey cradled her doll and smiled.

Screams of rage from the Troop. "You can't be secretary if you don't write down the minutes."

"Yeth I can. You elected me. I don't have to write it down. I can remember it, can't I, Dolly?"

In order to keep them from exterminating their newly elected secretary, I suggested that we talk about the Out-of-Doors.

We explored the kind of clothes we thought we should wear to school, and to town, and out to play in the woods, skipped "a compass" because I didn't know how to use one myself, and eventually progressed to Trail Signs which gave Gretchen and Linda and Wendy a long awaited opportunity to describe in infinite detail how they had strayed from the paths of righteousness, got stuck in the blackberry bushes and how scary it was to be scratched by brambles.

At the end of this wandering saga, Peggy said, "Well, you didn't follow the Trail Signs. A Girl Scout's supposed to obey orders. I move that we make a whole set of Trail Signs and put them on the mantel so Gretchen and Linda and Wendy will never be stuck again and Diana won't get lost. Diana! Pay attention!"

Diana was painting a yellow butterfly in her Nature notebook. She didn't even look up, but she did murmur, "I don't want to."

Peggy put her hands on her hips. "Diana Lamson! You make me sick! You don't even come to the meetings if you don't want to and you never pay any attention. You're the very one who ought to make every single Trail Sign all by yourself. *You* were the one who left your Buddy—"

Diana looked up and smiled at me. "I'm sorry. I suppose I should. All right, Peggy, I'll make the Trail Signs." She looked vaguely around the room. "We could use our rock collection and our driftwood collection if we can't go outdoors."

We used our collections and made fancy Trail Signs for which Diana painted labels indicating their meaning. "Gee, Diana, those are sure neat! You're good when you want to be." Diana nodded. She had found a bug on one of the pieces of driftwood and was examining it with rapt attention.

It was almost five o'clock when Susan and the fourth-graders came downstairs shedding sweetness and light in all directions as they put their original designs in their cigar boxes. Phyllis came over to me and, in a voice oozing honey, said, "Would it be too much trouble, Mrs. Jay, to explain to the younger children, just how two Troops would work? We're almost Intermediates now and we have so much to do, we just won't be able to help the little ones any more."

The little ones bristled, and Peggy stamped over to Phyllis. "I'm president of our Troop now, Mrs. Smarty, and we don't even want to be part of your old Troop. We don't need any help."

She flicked her skirt and turned back to the Brownies. "Okay, you guys, show those Intermediates how to make a Goodnight Tunnel and make it snappy."

This time it was Susan who was too stunned to speak.

12

LITTLE GRAINS OF SAND—

T HE first meeting in February, as both Troops were getting ready to go home, Phyllis asked us if it would be too much trouble if they all met in the gameroom next time. "We want to make Valentines." She smiled winningly at the glowering Peggy. "Wouldn't you like to meet with us? You'd get lots more Valentines—"

"We'd have to vote on it. Come on, you guys—" Peggy led her Troop into the laundry room.

"Isn't she cute?" Phyllis asked. "Doesn't she make a good president? My, I'll never forget the first time I was elected."

They came back into the gameroom and Peggy said, "We think it's okay, but just this once, remember."

I prepared for this joint meeting by helping our daughters make a mobile with different sized hearts hanging by threads from a coathanger. I thought it was quite fetching, but my offspring said it would work much better if we used little pieces of wood like they did in school when they made mobiles. I also made three dozen cupcakes with a new recipe which I started to explain to the Homemakers (they already knew about it, they'd made cupcakes a hundred times and anyway Gloria was bringing a heart cake which the baker made and she decorated)—in the vain hope that the "Tenderfeet" would wish to go upstairs and decorate cupcakes instead of remaining downstairs and gumming up my Troop with Sweet Reason.

Susan had produced the lace paper doilies in three sizes, a roll of red shelf paper, and five boxes of stickers in the shape of flowers. "For you, Honey," she said, handing me an enormous lace paper-edged heart. Within a circlet of pansies was tenderly inscribed:

> Roses are red,
> Violets are blue,
> I'm weak-minded,
> But so are you.

The "Tenderfeet" glanced at it and said they'd made lace paper Valentines like that millions of times, only their poem wasn't the same. It was—

While the Brownies were pouring in, I told Susan that Vi and Murph appreciated us even if the mothers didn't. "Vi told me this morning that their mourners' bench had no little girls sitting on it nowadays, only little boys. Isn't that heartwarming?"

"It's heartwarming all right, but is it—" Susan was counting Brownies. They were grouped in front of the fireplace, their hands cupped around hot cocoa, their feet stretched out toward the fire, their cheeks flushed, and their eyes shining as they talked over the Valentines they were going to make, and get.

"Twenty-two, twenty-three—they aren't all here yet. We've just got to have two meetings a week." She sat back and sighed. "I too was at the grocery store this morning. I ran into Mrs. Bean, booted and spurred, about to charge off to her first meeting. She reminded me that she is chairman of our Troop Committee. 'It is our thinking, Mrs.

Blake, that we should have a mothers' meeting as soon as possible,' she said. I just blinked like a wary toad and waited. 'It is our thinking that, as most of our mothers work, we should hold this meeting at night.' I began tossing sand in the gears. 'No more meetings,' I said, 'too many meetings now. Whole country's meeting crazy.' She said, 'Mothers *want* to meet.' I said, 'They do, but we don't,' and her machine came to a grinding halt." Susan grinned, "She looked very much like Phyllis as she drew herself up and said, 'Mrs. Blake!'

"Apparently the dear mothers have been calling her up also. Among other things, they gave her a pretty harrowing version of our Trail hike. By the time she got hold of it, we were planning to lure their little ones off and turn them loose in the Olympic mountains. Twenty-four, twenty-five —where's Mari?"

I'd been dreading this question. "She's bringing the new ones—"

"New ones! Mary, if you've been a Friend to All again—"

No, for once I was not the guilty one. These new Brownies were from the Council. Pat Smith had called and said there was an excellent Scout Leader who had just moved into our neighborhood, a Mrs. Green. She had two younger daughters who were transfers from another Troop, Reba and Rena. Reba was ten and almost ready to Fly Up and Rena was in the third grade. Mrs. Green worked for the Port of Embarkation during the day and held her Scout meetings at night. She was a Negro.

Susan nodded. "Good—"

I swallowed. "Miss Raite, Sally's teacher, called and asked if we could include May Chinn. She's a Chinese. Miss Raite feels that May might be more cooperative in school if she knew the Brownies wanted her."

Just as I finished speaking, Mari and Phyllis burst in, pushing before them two little dark Brownies. Mari said,

"Here they are, Mother. We'd like to introduce Reba and Rena Green, my mother and Mrs. Blake. We already took off their coats and galoshes and hung them up to dry."

The dark Brownies grinned showing white teeth and deep dimples, saluted, and followed Phyllis over to the group in front of the fire.

Mari cupped her hands and whispered, "They're really and truly Brownies, aren't they, Mother. Aren't they cunning?" They were, they were the cunningest children I have ever seen. Brownie dresses, skin the color and texture of sheared beaver, cheeks like ripe apricots, black eyes glistening with anticipation, hair in crisp little braids tied with neat brown ribbons. Brown from tip to toe, they squatted in front of the fire holding out delicate pink-tipped fingers.

Mari continued, "Oh, I forgot. We waited and waited for May Chinn, but I guess she isn't coming." She turned and ran over to join the group at the fire. Phyllis stood up and in a voice sweet as sugar said, "Peggy? Shall we show Reba and Rena what good Troops they're in by singing our opening song?"

Susan murmured, "She's coming along. In October she would have snapped, 'Okay, sing.'" It was true. The fourth-graders *were* coming along. They were showing signs of being really sweet and really considerate instead of sugar-coating iron wills.

They had just finished their song and gone to their tables, when in the door walked a tiny, bewitching sprite with licorice black hair, almond-shaped black eyes, who was wearing a bright red, high-necked Chinese dress and carrying a large black umbrella with a red rose on the handle.

"May! May!" My Troop broke into shouts of joy. "Did your grandfather say you could come? Can you be a Brownie too?"

May giggled. It was the sound a brook makes bubbling over stones. "I'm here, aren't I? Grandfather wasn't going to let me—" She danced over to the third-grade table and leaned over it. "—but I cried and cried, and wouldn't speak Chinese, until he called a taxi, and here I am."

I breathed, "Isn't she the most adorable—"

Susan murmured, "Just wait. I'm well acquainted with the Chinn family. Her grandfather is so soft-headed about her, he lets her have, and do, whatever she wants to. He's a Mandarin of the old school who brought up his own daughters as obedient Chinese ladies. May's mother died when she was born, and Grandfather Chinn is allowing this one to run wild."

While Susan was talking, May grabbed the ribbon off Durdey's curls and skipped around the table singing, "I'm a kite. I'm a kite. Can't catch me, I'm a kite."

A "Tenderfoot" caught her, took her by the arm and set her, rather firmly, down at the third-grade table. Quick as a flash she was up and off again, a shimmering prism, now here, now there, but always in mischief. She reached in the treat box, dug her finger in the cake and popped it into her mouth, whispering, "Don't tell. Don't tell." Not only did my Troop not tell, they leaned forward and watched her with broad grins, eyes gleaming with admiration. The Sweet Reason of the "Tenderfeet" began to be edged with impatience as they said, "Now May, Honey, sit down. Now, May, let Durdey's crayons alone. May! Give Gretchen back her Valentine!"

But Durdey grinned at Peggy, who nudged Sally, who giggled at Heidi, who said, "Boy! May's naughty!" and hunched up her shoulders in an ecstasy of admiration.

Before long my whole Troop was being just plain naughty. May picked up Peggy's Valentine, ripped off the lace paper and wore it as a hat. They all wore hats. May poked holes through Durdey's Valentine and held it up as a mask. They all wore masks. May used Gretchen's red paint as a lipstick. Their mouths were all smeared with red paint. Even Diana was drawing crooked hearts with hideous bug faces in the center and sending May into gales of laughter. The room rang with hysterical giggles which the "Tenderfeet" gave up trying to stop and just sat at their table, rigid with disapproval, and made Valentines.

We got through our first joint meeting somehow, stuffed our Valentine box with what was left after May's depredations, and were winding out in the Goodnight Tunnel when Susan mopped her brow. "Whew! Do you still feel Friendly to All?" Grabbing May's black umbrella before she poked Heidi's eye out, I snapped, "NO. We have one friend too many, and you know which one I mean."

Maybe it was May Chinn, and maybe I was tired out from all the confusion, but anyway, whatever the cause, I went upstairs from that meeting feeling as if I never wanted to see or hear of a Brownie again.

Mari and Sally were setting the table and making the salad, Heidi was feeding her zoo, and I was cooking dinner and wondering if it would be all right to freeze three dozen cupcakes, when the telephone rang. It was Gretchen's mother. Why were Gretchen's feet wet when she came home? Gretchen was subject to colds and why didn't I see to it that Gretchen's feet were kept dry. Perhaps if I didn't have so many *new* Brownies, I could see to it that the *old* Brownies didn't catch cold.

No sooner had I hung up than Colleen's mother called. Why were Durdey and Colleen so late getting home? Couldn't I get someone to drive the children home? She'd offer to, but Mickey took the car to work. Perhaps if I didn't have so many *new* Brownies, I'd be able to drive them all home.

No sooner had I hung up than Patty's mother called. Patty had crumbs in her braces. Patty wasn't supposed to eat cake. The orthodontist said that Patty was supposed to eat an apple when she came home from school. Why hadn't she eaten her apple? Would I please see to it that Patty ate her apple instead of cake. Perhaps if I didn't have so many *new* Brownies, I could watch Patty and Betty more carefully.

No sooner had I hung up than Reba and Rena's mother called. She just wanted to thank me for the wonderful time Reba and Rena had had. Weren't joint Troop meetings fun? She certainly was grateful to us for making room for Reba and Rena. It made them feel a part of their new neighborhood. Was there anything she could do to help? She worked during the day, but she had every evening off, except Thursday; that was Scout night. She knew I was busy cooking dinner and she didn't want to bother me, but she just called to let me know that she'd been a Brownie Leader for three years, and she was standing by, ready to do anything she could to help.

I was too overcome to say anything but "Thank you— thank you—thank you—thank you."

Then Susan called, incoherent with rage. "Mothers! What did I tell you. Gretchen and Linda and Wendy were crushed because May spoiled their valentines! Honestly! No matter what you try to do for their little darlings, mothers are never grateful, nor will they ever offer to help. Are we sure it's a good idea to have Negro children in our Troop? If they ever showed the least sign of appreciation—"

I told her about my hatful of complaints ending with my astounding call from Mrs. Green.

"No wonder! She's been a Brownie Leader. She knows what we're up against—"

"Susan? Don't you think we'd better have that mothers' meeting? We could at least explain what we're trying to do—"

Susan interrupted. "Why bother? Most of them work and the others quite obviously don't give one whoop as long as we continue to furnish nice, reliable child care. After this, when they complain, just tell them if they don't like the way we run our Troop, they're at liberty to form one of their own and run it the way they like."

"In other words, put up or shut up?" I asked.

"Exactly," Susan said. "I'll be over tomorrow afternoon so we can figure out some way to control May Chinn. There's no use calling Grandfather, because he refuses to speak English."

The next afternoon, Susan and I were having tea, hating mothers, and, as usual, hip-deep in Brownie guests, when Emily came bounding in, followed by Judy and Jody to ask us if we thought the Argyle socks she was knitting looked like Stan.

As all Emily's beaus looked as much alike to us as Argyle socks, we said, "Um-hum" and "My, they are good looking" and asked how she'd ever dreamed up such an original idea as knitting socks for Stan.

Emily flushed, "Well, you see, we think we might be going steady pretty soon."

At this news flash, Sally and Peggy converged on Emily and asked if Stan was the one with the blue '48 Dodge. Emily said yeah but they weren't to tell a soul. They said, Boy! they hoped she'd go steady with Stan, and rushed out to the kitchen to tell Mari and Phyllis the good news.

Emily slumped down on the couch beside us and began to knit. "How are your Brownies getting along?" she asked.

We told her we now had twenty-six Brownies and had tried to have a joint meeting which was a shambles. We took turns giving lurid descriptions of the meeting.

"Yowsie! Aren't about a dozen of them ready to Fly Up?" she asked.

Yes, about fifteen were almost ten and were—or should be—learning their Tenderfoot requirements.

"Why don't you have two Troops?" she asked, frowning

at a crooked red diamond. "Darn it, I'll bet I've done this wrong—"

We'd tried to have two Troops, in fact we actually did separate the girls into age groups, but we simply could not find any more Leaders.

Emily held up an Argyle sock roughly the length of a King Salmon and peered at it. "Why don't we help you? We're working on our Leader in Training Program and we're supposed to— Do you think this is long enough? Stan's got feet as big as skis—Judy and Jody and I'll help you—"

"But Emily, you have so much to do—"

I was interrupted by Judy and Jody who were sitting on the loveseat studying a movie magazine. "Yeah, there's studying, and the D.T. meetings, and Senior Stunt night, and Girls Club and Red Cross and United Good Neighbors and—"

Emily sat forward and glared at them. "Fine Leaders in Training you are. You're here right now, aren't you?"

Yeah, they were here right now but this wasn't Monday, and they were supposed to be at a chorus meeting and she knew it.

"After all Mrs. Blake and Mrs. Jay did for us! Helped with our Community Christmas tree and helped us sell our wreaths and let us dance in their gameroom practically every night. I'm certainly surprised at you!"

They were surprised too and meekly said anything Em thought was okay, was okay by them.

Emily sat back. "Don't give it another thought. We'll be here whenever you need us, rain or shine. 'Course we might not be able to come every Monday, 'cause Croaky'll have fits if we don't sing sometimes, but then you probably won't need us every time. Gosh, I wonder why Stan hasn't called. I told Mom to tell him to call me here—"

The telephone rang and Emily and Judy and Jody and

Mari and Phyllis and Peggy and Sally and Durdey and Heidi all rushed to answer it.

"Do you suppose they'd really come?" I asked in the deathly silence that followed their exodus.

Susan shrugged. "If they came once a month, or whenever we have a joint meeting, it would certainly solve a lot of our problems."

Emily and her comet tail came tearing back. She said that Stan would drive them to our house whenever we needed them and pick them up after the meeting and drive them home. "Stan's the greatest, really he is, just the greatest. My gosh, it's five o'clock and I told Mom I'd be home at four to cook dinner. See you. Don't forget to call us when you need us. 'Bye-ye."

That night the girls and Jim and I were having a rousing game of Scrabble when the telephone rang. It was Mymother calling to say that they were having a special meeting of the Troop Committee and mothers, and she would like Susan and me to meet with them at her house at eight o'clock the following evening. I said Susan and I would be there.

When I told Jim, he groaned, "This Brownie business is just getting to be too much. Do you have to be a Leader at night also?"

I said apparently, and now he knew how I felt when he went to medical meetings. He frowned, so I patted him soothingly and reminded him that he wouldn't be home anyway, Wednesday was staff dinner, and left the room again to call Emily to sit with the girls and to call Susan and tell her that Mrs. Bean had acted and was going to force the mothers to give us some help. "I just knew it. She had that interfering look in her eye when I saw her at the grocery store. I'll pick you up."

Wednesday evening, Susan came by about a quarter to eight. As I got into the car she said, "I hope you're well wrapped in rules and regulations. Something tells me there's a real storm brewing."

"I'm just going to tell them this is our Troop and we're going to run it our way," I said bravely.

"Innocent!" Susan pointed to a bulging folder. "I've spent all afternoon conferring with Mrs. Burton, bringing the Troop records up to date, memorizing Procedures, and preparing for the mothers."

I said she had a regular *thing* about mothers. I'd bet the Troop Committee would give us so much help that even Miss Dale would approve.

"You have a regular *thing* about Miss Dale," Susan retorted.

We stopped in front of Mymother's glacial squatting hen, and Susan said, "Modern mothers! That's the very worst kind!"

As we walked up the steps Susan said she was dying to see the inside of the Beans' house. She'd always wanted a modern house, but Charlie wouldn't hear of it. "Just one big quonset hut, with everything electric! That's my idea of heaven," Susan said.

Mrs. Bean opened the door, Susan beamed and said, "You have such a beautiful house!" and I began to feel marooned. While Mymother pressed a button in the paneling which slid back exposing a coat closet and Susan was still exclaiming, I glanced into the living room. Eleven mothers sat in rows of folding chairs, facing the Indian mask. In front of them in a little circle sat the Troop Committee, Mrs. Williams, Mrs. Johnson, Mrs. Drew. At one side sat Miss Dale! A tribunal!

As we hung our coats on hangers which grew like branches out of the closet wall, Susan glanced in the living room. "Storm Troopers!" she muttered, "You just wait! They won't stop until they get a full confession."

Mymother introduced us to everyone in the room and

then took her place back of a card table laden with forms and pamphlets from the Council. "As you know, we have had several Troop Committee meetings to discuss our neighborhood problem." She turned to us. "This evening we called our mothers' meeting at seven o'clock to prepare the questions we thought we would like to ask our Leaders. It is our thinking that we should begin by finding out just what is expected of a Scout Leader."

She read aloud "DO YOUR LEADERS MEET THESE STANDARDS?" When she had finished, she flattened her hands on the table and said, "I know you won't mind giving us your qualifications," and waited for us to acquit ourselves.

Susan began with an impressive dossier of her education, special training and experience as a playground instructor and substitute teacher in the primary grades. She seemed calm, dignified and courteous, but I know Susan and could tell from the set of her shoulders that she was mad enough to spit. When she sat down, the Storm Troopers nodded like puppets.

Mrs. Bean turned to me. "I know the mothers would be interested in knowing about your background."

I took the stand. Well, I'd ah—been to college for one year and one quarter where I'd ah—majored in ah—drama and minored in music. After I left College, I'd ah—worked as a secretary and then in a radio station—and ah—then in an advertising agency and ah—I'd married a doctor.

The Storm Troopers' expressions remained quizzical, so I reached wildly around in my mind for a soothing phrase from the Leader's Guide. "We have three daughters of Brownie age, and I like seven, eight, and nine-year-old girls and enjoy doing the things they like to do, and I feel that I am the person to be a Brownie Scout Leader!"

Their expressions indicated that they did not agree. My voice rose. "What's more, I enjoy it more than anything I have ever done, Susan and I both do, and, judging by the size of our Troops, our Brownies do too!" Just in time I swallowed "so there!" the Brownie clincher.

A brief smile flickered across Miss Dale's face.

Mymother's voice was detached. "We are not here to criticize, Mrs. Jay, we are here to help." The Storm Troopers nodded at her and at one another.

Mrs. Williams glanced at a notebook. "I assume you have both completed the training course?"

I snapped, "We've been too busy—"

Susan deftly interposed, "We have been working closely with the Leader's Guide which contains all the information available in the training course."

Again Miss Dale smiled.

Without pausing, Susan progressed smoothly into PRO-CEDURES and quoted PROGRAM, FIELD, ORGANIZA-TION and TRAINING. I was delighted to note that Mymother had to refer to her copy of PROCEDURES in order to follow Susan's rapid speech.

Mrs. Johnson asked, "How do you handle your Troop finances?"

While Susan gave a clear and lucid financial report, I comforted myself by thinking of the way we really handled our finances.

It was actually unnecessary for us to keep a Troop finance sheet as long as we had Jane, our loan shark, who could give from memory every penny we had ever collected and spent. Jane threatened the new members with debtor's prison if they forgot to bring their Membership dollar. She had burst out crying when we explained to her that new girls who joined in the middle of the year would only have to pay fifty cents. Wrenching ten cents for paste out of that human safety deposit vault was more difficult and debasing than trying to wheedle a loan from a bank without sufficient collateral. If Jane's Troop finance sheet didn't balance every week, she retired to her corner and refused to participate, even eat, until she had located the missing five cents. Now she was busily training Sally, who was already hounding the new members for their Membership dues and threatening to "tell Jane on you" if each one of her Troop members didn't cough up her five cents.

Susan finished, "Yes, I believe our Troop finances are in order."

There were murmurs to the effect that with such a large Troop we ought to be able to take the children skating, and on field trips—

Mrs. Drew pounced on me. "Mrs. Jay? Is it possible to prepare such a large Troop for the Intermediate program?"

"Fifteen of them will be ready to Fly Up and become Intermediates at the end of this year," Susan said and passed around her perfect individual records, while I thought of Sally and Durdey and Peggy who were going-on-nine, getting bossy and dictatorial, and were already quoting Scout Laws.

"Aren't the growth-gradients disturbing?" Mymother asked.

"Occasionally—" Susan began. I interrupted. "Of course they are, but we are *still* able to carry out the basic Scout program which is, to help them, to help themselves, to help others. We'd be able to do even more if we could arrange to have two meetings a week—"

The dam burst with a roar. "Why haven't you had a mothers' meeting to explain your needs? Why do you take in new members? Why do you include children from three grades? Why—why—why—why—?"

Susan tried to answer but the noise was horrendous, so she gave me the Desperate Leader's Look which meant I was to take off on a snipeflight of imagination as to "What'll we do now?"

I stood up and was recognized by Mymother. The flood waters receded to a low mutter. "We have plans for our mothers which we have been working on for some time. We are going to give a great big party!"

Susan's eyes widened as I continued. "Our Troop is not only unusually large and therefore unwieldly, it consists of a melange of races, creeds and colors. It is difficult to interest many of the parents in what we are trying to do because most of them are still pretty bewildered by the American family group consisting of one Brownie, one Cub, one Elk and one Episcópalian."

Miss Dale gave her sharp cry of laughter. The mothers smiled, but their eyes were wary.

"It is not only going to be a great big party, it is going to be quite an impressive ceremony," I continued. "A Senior Scout Troop has offered to help us and will wear full regalia to lend splendor to the occasion."

By this time Susan's mouth had dropped open and her brow was creased. She jumped as Mymother asked, "Have you discussed this program with your mothers?"

As I had been making it up as I went along, I said haughtily that it was our policy never to discuss anything with our mothers until we had completed our discussion with the Troop. "We do nothing that our Brownies do not wish to do. It is *their* Troop." Susan swallowed. I sat down.

Miss Dale leaned forward. "Do your older girls fully understand the meaning of their Scout Laws?" she asked.

"I'll say they do—" I began, and Susan interrupted, "We believe they do, but we do not put too much accent on repeating them in list form, because the younger children—"

There was an immediate wrangle over the latest methods of teaching, and many oblique references to memory versus meaning. While they were arguing, Susan and I held our customary low-voiced conference.

"You and your great big party! What ever gave you that idea?" Susan muttered.

"I had to do something. They were about to stand us up against the wall and shoot us."

"Memory versus meaning. They'll keep us here all night."

"No, they won't. I'm going to get up and tell them." I stood up and was recognized by Mymother. In the chesty voice so much admired by the drama section, I began, "This is the way we teach the Scout Laws. Our Brownies learn HONOR by hearing Minnie say, 'That's the last time I'll ever tell you a secret, Colleen. You're a regular old blabbermouth and besides you cheat. Girl Scouts don't cheat!'

"They are learning LOYALTY by hearing Patty say, 'I don't care if Katie does sniff. She has a cold and she's in our Troop, and we like her. Girl Scouts like every single person in the whole Troop. So there!'

"They are learning to be USEFUL and HELPFUL by watching Cherie drop her dainty embroidery to patiently thread needles, hold edges together, and make countless French knots, no matter how many times they call, 'Cherie, commere. You gotta help me next.'

"They are learning to understand one another and to be as good friends as any group of females ever will be by discovering that Reba and Rena and Sumiko and Kaziko and May Chinn, not only have different colored skins, but they have different games which are new and exciting.

"They are learning COURTESY as we all learn it, by trial and error, by being ignored when we are discourteous, and accepted when we are kind.

"They are learning to know and love animals because our house is crawling with them and they are as much a part of our Troop as the Brownies themselves.

"They are learning to be obedient because they get into trouble when they aren't.

"They are cheerful, because all children are basically cheerful when they are busy and interested.

"They are learning to be thrifty because they have to be,

and because Jane and Sally guard the funds and fight tooth and nail to protect them.

"They are as clean in thought, word and deed as any other heterogeneous group of American children, which is, on the whole, pretty clean.

"Yes, I'd say they were learning, but not one of them is learning half as much as Susan and I are, and they'd be able to learn a lot faster if we were allowed to split our Troop into two meetings a week, and could get some new Leaders!" Red-faced and panting, I sat down.

Wintry smiles greeted my defense, and immediately conflicting opinions on discipline versus permissive techniques, large versus small groups, two versus one Troop, were loud and acrimonious. Susan and I sat there like backboards while they bounced theoretical tennis balls off us.

Miss Dale got up and came over, and we made room for her between us on the morgue slab. Her voice was also the low murmur of the experienced Scout Leader.

"That was an impassioned speech, Mrs. Jay." Her light gray eyes were no longer chilly but dancing with suppressed laughter. "*If* we help you form two Troops, will you and Mrs. Blake do something for us?"

"We will do anything as long as we don't have to turn away cold, wet Brownies," I said.

She paused a minute. "Pat Smith is starting a new training class. It begins Friday, lasts from ten until three, and is to be held at the Rainier Field House. There will be six sessions. Will you go?"

Certainly, we'd be glad to go.

"Will you see to it that there is at least one adult to every six Brownies when you take a field trip?"

Certainly we would.

She took some notes out of her purse and stood up. "Mrs. Bean? Ladies? It is my understanding that your Troop Committee fully comprehends what is expected of it. We feel that there should be two Brownie meetings a week. Will you make the necessary calls, or appoint a committee to make the necessary calls? Mrs. Jay and Mrs. Blake have indicated they would prefer to have one Troop on Monday and one Troop on Wednesday."

This was authority speaking, now the eyes were interested and eager.

Miss Dale glanced at her notes. "You will form a committee to provide transportation whenever necessary, will help to secure new Leaders, or mothers to act as assistant Leaders, will help with outdoor activities, Troop finances, special events, and camp plans. In other words, you will give Mrs. Jay and Mrs. Blake the backing they need in the community. Is that correct?"

The Storm Troopers nodded and the mothers blinked. "Now, if you'll excuse me, I have some work to finish at the Council—"

Mymother said, "Just a moment, Miss Dale. It is our thinking also, we have had several meetings on this point, that we should have a meeting of the Troop Committee and the Leaders at least once a week, and of the Troop Committee and the Leaders and the mothers at least once a month—"

"NO!" Susan said flatly.

There was a little flutter from the mothers of "There are so many meetings now—"

Miss Dale looked thoughtfully at Susan and me. "I don't think that is necessary. At the Council we find that too much accent on organization is often followed by diminution of interest, particularly in highly organized areas. I believe that your Leaders would prefer to feel free to call on you whenever they feel it is necessary. Now if you will excuse me—" She turned and strode out of the room.

I said, "But Susan! She's marvelous—"

Susan nudged me. "She's not a mother. That's why."

The mothers were all talking at once. "I had no idea—but it's so complicated—I can't even manage three, let alone sixteen—Of course I'm willing to do anything to help—"

Mymother tapped her fingers on the card table. "I suggest then that the Troop Committee procure a list of volunteers and that we meet once a month to coordinate our activities. Our Leaders may feel free to call on us at any time and to attend these meetings whenever they like and to call a special meeting whenever needful." She turned to us. "Does that meet with your approval?" We nodded. "Very well. I feel that this meeting has been worth while and has accomplished a great deal in the way of understanding of our local needs. If there is no further business, let us adjourn and have some refreshments."

She went out to the kitchen and came back carrying a blue plastic philodendron leaf on which reposed a square plate of fig newtons and square cups of coffee, pale and obviously caffeinless.

I was still smoldering at mothers who secretly tattled to the Troop Committee and the Council and then publicly put us on the spot, but Susan was speaking to each mother, making necessary brief explanations as to why we must divide the Troop and generally being Friendly to All.

While the Troop Committee was asking for volunteers, Susan said to me, "Come on. Let's get out of here so they can see who is the biggest and best civic martyr and talk about us. Come on."

On the way home I was grumbling at the injustice of it all, when Susan asked, "What's the matter? Don't you like mothers' meetings? Actually these weren't bad, as mothers go—"

"Why, Susan Blake!" I fumed. "The whole thing was outrageous—"

"Now, now. 'Little drops of water, little grains of sand—make the mighty ocean—and the pleasant land.' Let's go

down to the Council tomorrow morning and register both
Troops."

It was mighty restful to sit in Pat Smith's office and complain to my heart's content about recalcitrant Brownies and
ungrateful mothers and what a great, big martyr I was,
while Susan filled out the forms. At each new outburst Pat
nodded sympathetically and, when I got too far out in the
weeds, led me gently back to the point, which was, "Can
you handle two Troops?"

"Yes, you may use Emily and Judy and Jody as assistant
Leaders, but I think you should invite an occasional mother
to see what you're trying to do. Yes, you may have joint
meetings once a month or so. Yes, yes, yes, yes—"

No complaints. No criticisms. Just the nice, warm,
friendly Council and Pat Smith's empathy and knowledge-
able cooperation.

"Peace! It's wonderful!" Susan said as she handed Pat the
completed forms for two Brownie Troops.

13

BLACK JELLY BEAN

O'D like to be able to say that I was so pitifully grateful to Miss Dale for allowing us to have two Troops, that I threw myself into the training class and became an ideal Scout Leader in six weeks.

As a matter of fact, by Friday morning it was beginning to dawn on me that two Brownie meetings, plus a training class every week, was going to be quite tricky to handle.

Never a ray of sunshine the first thing in the morning, I was crabbier and more disorganized than usual as I pushed Jim and the children out the door and rushed around putting the house in order, muttering to myself, "Ten o'clock! Who ever dreamed up a training class for mothers at ten o'clock in the morning. I'll bet Miss Dale did. Of course *she* doesn't have beds to make or dishes to wash. *She* probably lives in an apartment hotel. *She* doesn't have any children, so it never occurs to *her* that it is Friday and I haven't even finished the ironing—"

I drove over to pick up Susan, who seemed cheerful, well organized, and bursting with vitality. As usual, it was raining and to the slip-slap, slip-slap of the windshield wiper,

I grumbled, "I just know we are going to play games. I have a psychic block against games of any kind. And no wonder, my father used to jerk us all out of bed at six o'clock in the morning, even in Butte when it was ten below zero, and make us run around the block taking deep breaths."

"And you haven't taken one since." Susan chuckled.

"Not only that, but he used to get us up at six o'clock to play tennis and jump hurdles and take back flips—"

"Wouldn't hurt you now." Susan eyed my waistline.

"Not only that, but he made us play guessing games at meals."

"Maybe if my father had been more like that, I wouldn't have felt called upon to be the biggest girl athlete in college."

"I hate crafts too. And no wonder! How would you like to have spent your whole childhood sitting still on trains, cutting out Letty Lane paper dolls—"

"I thought you said you were running around the block—" Susan burst out laughing. "The trains sound wonderful to me. I was born right in our neighborhood and expect to die right there. I'd never even been to Idaho till Charlie took pity on me and drove me to Pocatello."

When we stopped in front of the Field House, Susan said, "Well, well, well. My old stamping ground. Many's the hour I've spent chasing mothers out of that playfield. Just wait till Charlie hears I've given myself up and am re-entering prison of my own accord."

"Didn't you tell him we were taking training?" I asked.

"Heavens, no. He's bitter enough about the amount of time I spend with the Brownies. Did you tell Jim?"

"I didn't dare. He'd just say, 'Hamper, hamper, hamper. I thought you were going to improve your mind.'"

The training room was large and chilly. It contained a scrubbed fireplace with one dusted log, a long bare table, a blackboard, and fifteen mothers who sat in chairs against the wall, clutching "nosebags," notebooks and small children and eyeing one another, tense and wary.

"Looks as if you weren't the only one who disliked sports," Susan murmured. "Let's sit over here in the corner."

Pat Smith came in, glanced around the room and grinned. "If you could just see your suspicious expressions. This isn't dangerous, it's fun!" She placed a suitcase on the long bare table. "Maybe we'd better start with the Brownie system for getting acquainted. Brownies aren't old enough to be self-conscious, they ask what they want to know. They walk up to a new girl and say, 'What's your name? Where do you live? Have you got any sisters and brothers? How old are you?' Personally, I think it's a social technique which would vastly improve most adult gatherings. Suppose you turn to the person on your left, pretend you're a Brownie, and ask whatever you want to know. Then, remembering these facts, introduce her to the next person."

She kept one eye on our tentative efforts while she got out the familiar Sing Together, Games for Girl Scouts, Leader's Guide, and pamphlets. Almost immediately the room began to lose its chilly atmosphere and to be warmed by laughter and friendliness.

I turned to the woman on my left who was valiantly trying to corral two fat, black-eyed imps about three and four years old. "What's your name?"

"Effie Bernstein, Ronnie come back here, he goes to meetings with me all the time—went to a P.T.A. Board meeting last night, slept all through it—we live at, Sandra quit that, here, give me your coat, Lander and Powell, big white house on the, tie Ronnie's shoe, Sandra—I'm twenty-five and I have three, Ronnie take your fingers out of your mouth, Jeanie—she's the Brownie, Sandra, quit staring, wants to go to Camp so that's why, Ronnie sit still, I'm here—"

I gave my life history, left and right, and by the time we

had all introduced ourselves, there was as much hilarity as there was at our Brownie meetings.

Pat Smith held up three fingers. Nothing happened, so she yelled, "QUIET" in a fair imitation of Phyllis' stentorian tones, which immediately produced silence and startled expressions. Pat said, "This is the Scout Silence Sign. Believe me, it is useful at Troop meetings, and no family dinner table should be without it.

"Those of you who already have Troops probably cannot understand why they seem to increase in the spring, faster than rabbits. You may have wondered if you had developed unusually fascinating personalities. I assure you it isn't so, and even if it were, Brownies couldn't care less." She grinned, rocked back on her heels, and the mothers burst into laughter.

Susan nudged me. "I'll bet you thought it was because you were so darned sweet—"

I had, so I said, "Don't be ridiculous."

Pat Smith continued, "Brownies join Troops for many reasons; some just want to join something, some belong because their friends do, some are attracted by the uniform, some are urged by their parents, some come to learn new things. But in spring, they come because they want to go to Camp." She picked up the Camp folder. "Many of you have already taken your Brownies on Cookouts and hikes and trips to the Out-of-Doors to prepare them for Camping. Right here I want to emphasize two very important things. Always use the Buddy system. Never allow them to go anywhere alone. Few things happen to two children, and if anything does, the Buddy can always run back and get help."

I thought of the day we lost Diana and shuddered. Even the Buddy system didn't always work.

"Always get parent permission slips. I assure you that a mother who seems to be the most cooperative is the first to leap to a lawyer if her child is injured while she is with you."

"Mothers!" Susan snorted and wrote, "Get permission slips" in her notebook. I was thinking of our hikes. Susan at the head and I at the tail of twenty capering Brownies who hid in the trees and popped out to scare us. Sometimes they disappeared until we found them crouched over a bug or a leaf. Sometimes we didn't run across the explorers until we started to count noses before going home and had to send a search party out for them. We had never obtained a special permission slip. The "Tenderfeet" occasionally demanded the Buddy system, but only because the smaller children melted away from them like snow from around hot pokers.

Pat Smith caught my wandering attention. "—a cold, wet Brownie isn't having any fun and she's probably catching cold. Don't hover over her. Make her remember her own raincoat and galoshes. Make her self-reliant. Safety-Mindedness is developed in discussions at Troop meetings. We all know that no matter how careful we are, accidents can and do happen—"

I remembered the day I had casually scooped up five Brownies and taken them to the market. What if one of them had been run over or lost or hurt? I'd been so delighted by their response to the colorful sights and tastes and smells, it had never occurred to me to be apprehensive. When was a Brownie not a Brownie?—

So Safety-Mindedness was developed by discussion, was it? At our Troop meetings Susan and I both clucked continuously, "Don't run with scissors in your hand, hold your knife with the point down, don't run across the street. Walk, and look both ways," but to Brownies those were mother sounds and as unarresting as the patter of rain.

Susan nudged me. "Now stop it. I can tell by your expression that you're imagining some ghastly thing. We've never had any real trouble. Stop worrying and pay attention."

I tried to attend, but the more I heard, the more my apprehension grew. The training class versus the Leader's Guide, was the difference between correspondence school and college. Eventually one learned both ways, but it would be ghastly to hurt a Brownie in the process.

Pat Smith went on with a discussion of the Out-of-Doors, or preparation for Camp. Her warnings were like stop lights in my imagination. "The most important step in First Aid is prevention"—How did you prevent a child from leaping off a wall and breaking her ankle?—"Teach them what a compass is and how to use one"—If they were lost in the woods, they couldn't eat a compass—"Trail signs are simple and recognized by Girl Scouts, Boy Scouts, and Forest Rangers, but they must be accurate so that in the event a child does become lost, the Trail signs can be followed until she is located"—Didn't Miss Dale tell me to obliterate Trail signs as we went along? How could a search party follow obliterated Trail signs? I was going to find out the answers to these questions before we had one more Brownie meeting. Miss Dale needn't worry. From now on Friday was the most important day of my week.

It seemed like moments, but was actually two hours later, when Pat Smith said, "I think we've had enough dire warnings for today. Everybody bring a nosebag? The coffee's ready, ten cents a cup, let's have lunch."

While we were eating, Effie Bernstein said, "Gee! I won't let the kids go to the park near our house. They caught one of those m-e-n, mind your own business, Ronnie, last week scaring the k-i-d-s, no, I'm not talking about that awful man, Sandra, wipe your mouth, and is our whole neighborhood ever worked up!"

The park near her house turned out to be our Park where we had allowed our Brownies to romp and play. By the time she finished spelling out the ghastly details, I was so worked up I was tempted to tell Susan that from now on we'd tuck our Brownies under our feathers and huddle in the gameroom for the remainder of the year.

When we had finished lunch, Pat Smith said, "This afternoon we are going to play games. Today's Brownie has such a crowded schedule with schoolwork, music and dancing lessons, concerts, movies, and TV, the most important thing a Troop can do for her is to offer her a chance to play. We'll start with Raisin Relay." Out of her capacious suitcase, Pat took a box of raisins and a box of toothpicks. At the sight of them I could feel myself turning to stone. "We will form two Teams. The leader of each Team has a saucer of raisins and each player has a toothpick. On signal, the leader spears three raisins on her toothpick and feeds them to the next person in line. She then passes her saucer to the person next to her. The Team that finishes eating its raisins first, wins. Ready?"

I loathe raisins.

The next game was Pony Express. Susan and I were chosen as leaders, which meant that Susan stood several yards in front of our Team and I stood several yards behind. On signal the first runner ran to Susan who gave her a verbal message requiring an answer. The runner delivered her message to the next in line until it reached the last player who wrote the message down and delivered it to me. I was supposed to give a verbal reply which, when written down by the first runner, was delivered to Susan. The reason I said, "Lapland" instead of "Happy Landings" was that I was appalled by the difference in Pony Express as played by a Brownie Troop and by a group of mothers. So often had I watched the light, gay children flitting back and forth on the tips of their toes, dancing with impatience until it was their turn, giggling delightedly at the change in words. Now, at the back of the line, I was getting the full effect of a leaden row of self-conscious adults, standing on their heels, pulling down their girdles, patting their hair, and giggling foolishly as they repeated over and over again, "Oh, was I supposed to go next?"

I loathed Pony Express played by Leaders.

The games went on and on and on. I was so nervous and distraught I couldn't walk a straight line, let alone follow my feet through field glasses, and it didn't help to watch Susan moving as effortlessly as a leopard, her eyes shining with the light of conquest as her Team easily won any game except the ones in which I was involved.

The last game was Jelly Bean. A plate of jelly beans was passed and *then* I learned that the white beans were exempt and each holder of a colored bean was to do a trick! The death wish being uppermost in my mind, I had chosen the black one, only to find that black meant, "Do a dance!"

I grimly arose and was writhing around in an East Indian dance, wishing that I really and truly were a widow and could toss myself on a burning ghat, while Susan eyed me like a Hollywood producer and said, "Not bad, not bad, considering the shape you're in," when I was rescued by having the door to the training room open.

A small dusty woman in a tweed suit, carrying a large felt bag, some books and what appeared to be an enormous pottery water jar, walked across the room, murmuring softly, "—was working in the pottery and didn't realize what time it was. I'm sorry to interrupt." She pushed at her hair and released a shower of hairpins, knelt and picked one or two of them up and jammed them in any old way, and wandered vaguely over to a chair, sat down and began to examine the jar, her brow furrowed in a critical frown.

"I think that's enough for today," Pat Smith said, smiling sympathetically at my tortured crimson face. "Any questions?"

Without taking her eyes off her vase, the small dusty woman continued, "—was wondering if there was anything— I couldn't attend the mothers' meeting so I called the Council—suggested that I come here today—no, I'm afraid this will have to be reglazed."

Diana's mother! I went over and introduced myself to Mrs. Lamson and said I was so glad to have Diana in our Troop.

She rubbed the side of the jar thoughtfully. "—bubbles. That's odd, I thought that fire was hot enough. What?" She raised large brown eyes and stared just a little beyond my left shoulder. "Oh, Mrs. Jay? I meant to call you. Diana told me she left you alone in the park. I was distressed and said, 'Oh, Diana, how can you be as you are?' "—her eyes dropped to the jar again, "Maybe the cone wasn't right—"

Susan's eyes were glinting with laughter as she stood looking down at Mrs. Lamson. "Genes," she mouthed and shrugged. Meanwhile Pat Smith was being showered with questions. "What do you do when your Leader hogs all the credit?" Susan murmured, "Mine did, but I just kept hacking her down to size." Pat Smith answered, "A Leader isn't interested in credit, she is interested in helping her Brownies grow into self-reliant, useful young women."

"What do you do when the mothers won't help?" another asked.

Pat Smith said, "Perhaps they don't help because you haven't asked them to." Susan murmured, "Or because they're mothers," and Pat continued, "Quite often it is because they've never seen a Brownie Troop and do not understand what you are trying to do. Usually if you invite them to attend a meeting—"

Diana's mother murmured, "And so I asked Diana if she thought the Brownies would be interested in having me show them how to make pottery, but she—" her voice trailed off.

A tall woman named Mrs. Miller, with an alert, attractive face and a big chignon of blonde hair, said, "How do you go about getting enough Brownies to form a Troop?"

"WHAT?" Susan and I gasped in unison.

Mrs. Miller said she had just moved to the city. Her furniture hadn't arrived yet, so she was more or less camping. She had been a Girl Scout Leader in Philadelphia and would like to continue out here. She had two daughters who were Brownies, but she knew so few people she had no idea how to go about forming a Brownie Troop. "If any of you—"

Susan and I leapt at her, introduced ourselves, said we lived right near her and would adore to have her help us. Why didn't she come to our meeting on Monday and bring her two little girls? It's a wonder we didn't scare her off by our eager offers of furniture, bedding, anything for a good old Scout Leader.

Pat Smith came over and listened to this remarkable situation. "Yes, why don't you help Mrs. Jay and Mrs. Blake, at least until you become accustomed to our Western way of life? I can assure you that by the time the news gets around that you are a Scout Leader, you will have more Brownies than you know what to do with."

Mrs. Miller promised to bring her daughters and come to our house on Monday afternoon, at which time we were going to formally announce the division of our Troop. Then I asked Pat if it was permissible to allow Senior Scouts to be assistant Leaders.

"Certainly. We have a new Leader in Training Program which has turned out some pretty efficient assistant Leaders. The list is available at the Council for any of you who are interested." She looked around the room, her eyes resting momentarily on each face. "It is almost impossible to condense everything you need to know into six Fridays. However, we have done the best we can. Meanwhile the Seniors can be Program Aides. I can't emphasize enough that the moment Camp is announced, new Brownies will just pop up out of the ground. Please don't miss a session if you can possibly avoid it. Any more questions? See you all next Friday."

While Pat was packing up her suitcase, Mrs. Miller was talking to us. "How many Brownies do you have?" she asked.

"Oh, I dunno. Every meeting is different—twenty-five—thirty maybe—" Susan said.

She gasped. "I had ten in Philadelphia! How on earth do you manage?"

Before I could speak, Susan said, "Why don't you wait until Monday afternoon and find out?"

14

CENTRAL CASTING

$\mathcal{M}$RS. MILLER'S introduction to our Brownie Troops was successful because Emily and Jody and Judy had completed their Leader in Training Program, *not* because Susan and I spent the week end after our first training class singing, "Wishing will make it so."

All the way home from the Field House, I burbled. "We'll trap Mrs. Miller, and with Emily, Jody and Judy we'll have six Leaders! Maybe we can even have three Troops—"

"Take it easy," Susan said, "this is one Troop meeting where we're going to have to behave like teachers. In the first place, we have to tell them that we are having two meetings a week. We'd better get together over the week end, plan every moment of the meeting and run it off just like a movie. Say! I've got an idea! Why not borrow Sweet Reason and get Jim and Charlie to make us another table and benches. Then if we do have three Troops—"

"—and when the children arrive, we'll give them hot cocoa, seat them at the tables according to age, and put them to work. Why not ask the Homemakers to go upstairs and make hot gingerbread for the treat! Mrs. Miller's eyes will really widen when she sees how well they can cook—"

"—and the third graders can plant their seeds!"

"—and the little ones can work on their sand garden. Even Mrs. Miller will have to admit that those seaweed trees are really something—"

Jim and Charlie didn't care to be run off like a movie. They said, "Why can't a man have one day off?" and "Do we have to spend every Sunday doing something for those— uh—Brownies?" and "What do you want another table for?" and "Why don't you get rid of a few instead of adding more Leaders?" But Sweet Reason prevailed, and they spent Sunday comparing notes on their addlepated wives and building another table and two benches. We planned to line the tables up end to end in the gameroom and form an island down the center with just room enough on either side for six Leaders to walk up and down and admire.

Phyllis was spending the week end with Mari, Durdey was spending the week end with Sally, and Peggy and Susan and Charlie were helping us spend Sunday getting ready for the all-important meeting.

While Jim and Charlie were working on the tables, Susan and I were out on the back porch lacquering egg cartons, sorting seed packages and discussing how to impress Mrs. Miller, while the children were sifting dirt and listening.

Several times Mari and Phyllis said, "Why don't we have our regular meeting and go upstairs like we always do?" and "How do you know the 'Tenderfeet' want to make gingerbread?" and "Can't we do leather? We've made gingerbread a million times, and it takes too long to cook."

We waved their objections away until finally, about three o'clock, they said they were going over to Emily's and see what Emily thought about our crazy old plans for *their* meetings.

Sally and Peggy and Durdey and Heidi were tired of sifting dirt and filling egg cartons. They didn't see why they had to do it for the whole darn Troop. Sally said, "Why can't we give our Leader play for Mrs. Miller? You promised us we could give our Leader play the very first time we had a new Leader."

Their Leader Play, which they had written the week end they were making the gameroom curtains, had long been a bone of contention. Two or three times each month, they had asked why we didn't invite a new Leader so they could give their Leader play, but what with Christmas and splitting up the Troop and Valentine's Day, we kept putting them off.

In order to whet their appetites for dirt sifting, I said to Susan, "Why not end this all-important meeting with their Leader Play?"

Heidi bristled. "Why don't I take all my animals down and make an exhibit? You said I could have one some day when Mrs. Blake got used to animals. She's been used to them ever since she saw Diana's old butterfly. She told me so."

I said, "Now look here, Heidi, if you're going to come to the Brownie meetings, you're going to behave like a Brownie. Do as I say and don't argue."

"Who'd take care of me if I didn't come?" Heidi countered.

Susan dropped a protective arm around her. "I think an animal exhibit would lend an aura of informality which the meeting might otherwise lack." Over Heidi's head she mouthed, "We're building tension," and added, "Come on, Heidi, let's go see the guinea pigs." They walked over and squatted down in front of the cages on the corner of the porch and admired Goldi and Locks, while I smiled fondly at them and wondered if I'd ever turn into the inspired Leader Susan was.

It was five-thirty by the time we had finished arranging everything for the meeting, so everybody stayed for supper. After supper we were sitting around the fireplace going over our plans, presumably to get the benefit of Jim and Charlie's advice.

Jim said, "Six Leaders and around thirty Brownies, two dogs, one cat, one parakeet, two rabbits, two guinea pigs, not to speak of assorted goldfish and turtles. That meeting ought to be noisier than a political convention."

Charlie asked, "What time is the Leader's Play going to start?"

We said we thought about five or five-fifteen. Mrs. Bean had promised transportation, so it didn't matter if we went a little overtime.

Charlie grinned. "I think I'll try to be here. I've seen one or two rehearsals and I'm sure that play's due for a long run."

Jim said, "Reserve me a seat too."

Sally and Peggy and Durdey looked up from their dolls long enough to say it sure was a neat play.

Mari and Phyllis were sitting at a bridge table in the corner making lists. Phyllis looked and sounded exactly like Mymother as she said, "It is my understanding that we are to start with hot cocoa. It is our thinking that the Patrol System—"

"Not the Patrol System, Phyllis. Not until you're Scouts—" I began.

Mari interrupted. "Now, Mother. Don't worry, it isn't the regular Patrol System, it's a surprise that Emily thought up."

Phyllis continued, "It is my understanding that our Troop will make gingerbread for the treat, the third grade will plant seeds, and the second grade will work on the sand garden. Is that correct?"

We nodded and she tapped her pencil on her front teeth. "What are you and Mrs. Blake going to be doing?"

We were going to explain the Troops to Mrs. Miller and take her around the room and show her our exhibits.

Phyllis shook her head, "I think it would be better if our Troop did that, while you explained our records to Mrs. Miller."

Charlie laughed. "I'd like to be around while you explain your records to an experienced Scout Leader." He stood up. "Susan, gather up your young. It's eight o'clock and you're going to have a big day tomorrow. Come on, Durdey, come on, Phyllis, we'll drive you home."

As they were leaving, Susan murmured, "Read your Handbook tonight. If I remember correctly, the Patrol System is not allowed until they are Girl Scouts."

"Susan? Would it be asking too much if we allowed Darleen and Sandra and Bettyjean and Sally Sue and Eloise to come?" Susan shook her head. "I can't hold out much longer—they call every single day—I did promise their mothers that the day we divided the Troops—and Sally promised them—" Susan sucked in her cheeks and pursed her lips— "it would save hours and hours of telephoning—it would show Mrs. Miller and the Seniors just how much we need help—"

There was a long pause. "You're absolutely besotted—" Susan shrugged. "Let 'em come—let 'em all come. We've long since ceased to have a Brownie Troop anyway—it's more like a riot." She grinned. "I'll call Pat Smith in the morning and find out how to get Patrols started with the older Brownies. See you at lunch—" Still shaking her head, she went out to the car.

Sally rushed to the phone to call Darleen and Sandra and Bettyjean and Sally Sue and Eloise, and after the usual shrieks of joy, I stuffed our daughters in bed, picked up Mari's Girl Scout Handbook and prepared to learn more about the Patrol System than was in the Leader's Guide. Obviously, we couldn't use the whole thing with the younger children, but sorting them into groups might serve as a junior aptitude test to see how advanced some of them really were in Brownie Scouting.

At three o'clock Monday afternoon, Mrs. Miller arrived, shepherding Edie and Helen, two little girls with slanting brown eyes, shoulder length blonde hair, and resplendently Brownie from head to toe. Edie was in the fourth grade, and Helen was in the second grade.

Susan and I took them downstairs and Mrs. Miller exclaimed over the size of the Troop meeting room and our equipment, while Edie and Helen ran over and began to admire Heidi's animal exhibit.

We explained our district with its preponderance of working mothers as a feeble excuse for allowing our Troop to grow so big, and gave even more tenuous reasons as to why we had not enlisted the help of mothers before this time. To all of this explanation Helen Miller listened with intent blue eyes. "Of course you can't give them opportunities for responsibility and ideals they can understand and accept when you have such a large group," she said.

"No, but you'll understand everything we have done, the moment you see them—" I said just as the mass of scuffling and dripping wet Brownies roared in and began jabbering, "Where is she? Where's the new Leader?"

"Sh-sh-sh- can't you see her?" The 'Tenderfeet" began slapping indiscriminately and shouting, "QUIET." Sally and Peggy herded in Darleen and Sandra and Bettyjean and Sally Sue and Eloise and shouted, "Here they are. We brought 'em—" The animals were chewing, mewing, squealing, and panting, and the Brownies were chewing, wrestling, squealing, and panting. Susan and I didn't dare look at Mrs. Miller as we wove in and out trying to calm them down, while Phyllis and Peggy bellowed, "QUIET! DON'T SLAP! YOU MIGHT HIT A LEADER BY MISTAKE!"

Into this bedlam walked Emily, Judy and Jody in full uniform, holding up three fingers. Dead silence!

Emily stepped forward. "Take your places, please." They scrambled to the tables dragging the new girls with them, climbed over the benches, sat down and folded their hands. "Scouts—attention!" Susan and I almost fainted when all thirty-six of them leaped to their feet, saluted, said, "How do you do, Mrs. Miller," and sat down.

Emily said, "Phyllis? Peggy? I believe you have important announcements to make." Phyllis stood and saluted. "My Troop wishes to meet on Monday, Mrs. Jay. We have made all the arrangements to surprise you." Peggy stood and saluted. "My Troop wishes to meet on Wednesday, Mrs. Jay. We have made all the arrangements to surprise you and Mother." She grinned at Susan and sat down.

Susan and I just stared.

Emily said, "Judy and Jody will pass the cocoa while I explain a very important part of Girl Scouting. It is called the Patrol System. You'll all have Patrols when you're Girl Scouts, so you might just as well learn about them now. Everybody ready to listen?"

They rested their chins on their hands and their elbows on the tables and fixed their eyes on Emily.

"Girl Scouts all over the world use the Patrol System. A Patrol is made up of four to eight girls. We will divide you up into groups of six, which will make six 'Patrols,' two at each table, but remember this isn't for real—that comes later. Today each 'Patrol' will choose a name. Are you divided up into second, third and fourth grades?" There was a little quick shifting and scurrying back and forth.

Emily's face broke into its bewitching grin. "In our Troop we chose the names of trees for our Patrols on account of we live in the Evergreen Playground, but you don't have to. You can choose any name for your 'Patrol' you want to." She resumed her serious expression. "At this meeting, because it is the first time you have seen Patrols, we will tell you what to do. Each Patrol is like a team. Each girl must do her share to make her Patrol the very best of all. Understand?"

They understood. Even their jaws were still.

"The fourth grade, when they Fly Up and turn into Intermediates, will have a Court of Honor which is made up of Patrol Leaders, assistant Patrol Leaders, the Troop scribe, the Troop treasurer, and the Troop Leader. They will have a special meeting once a week. Then when the rest of you Fly Up, you can have a Court of Honor too. The Court of Honor takes care of things which affect the whole Troop, like Saturday trips and Cookouts and camping trips, things like that. When you're a Brownie, you have to work awfully hard so as to get into the Court of Honor when you're a Girl Scout. You have to remember your Brownie Promise every day. Everybody know the Brownie Promise?"

Even the new ones joined the chant, "We-promise-to-help-other-people-every-day-especially-those-at-home."

Emily smiled. "That's right, and don't forget—"

They shook their heads. They'd *never* forget—

"Today we are going to form 'Patrols' so we'll be able to use them when we have joint meetings of our Troops, and we're going to choose our 'Patrol' names. Count off. The even numbers at each table form one 'Patrol,' and the odd numbers form the other. Doesn't that sound like fun?" It sounded like so much fun that the roaring and scuffling and slapping broke out again. Emily held up three fingers. Silence. "When you've decided on your 'Patrol' names, write them down on pieces of paper and bring them up to me. In Scouting, when we have a discussion like this, we call it a 'buzz.' Our buzzes are always very quiet—"

Instantly the noise fell to the drone of bees around a hive.

Emily came over to us. Her face wore the shining trust of a Brownie as she asked, "Isn't our surprise neat? I called Mrs. Bean and she called all the mothers last night and arranged the two meetings and then Phyllis and Mari and Colleen coached the kids at recess and at lunch on what to do. The Patrol System is the greatest, just the greatest."

Mrs. Miller said, "In Philadelphia we do not allow the Patrol System in Brownie Troops for reasons that are very much bound up with our reasons for insisting that the Troops should be small."

Emily looked down a moment and bit her lip. Then she looked directly at Mrs. Miller, adult charm radiating from her like sunshine. "Oh, we don't here either usually, until they're ready to Fly Up, but we have special problems in this district and I called Pat Smith last night, she's our District Director, and got special permission from the Council to explain Patrols to all of them today so the girls wouldn't feel so badly about having to split up their Troop." She stopped a moment. "You see, we've just completed our Leader in Training program, we're the first Senior Troop in the city to complete it, and we're Program Aides and this is our first opportunity to practice. Gee, it's going to be fun. I just love kids!" She had switched back to a child. "We sure think we're lucky to have a Scout Leader from Philadelphia. Gosh! I've never even been out of the State of Washington! What's it like to be a Scout in Philadelphia?"

Mrs. Miller gave a thumbnail sketch of a Scout Troop in Philadelphia, which sounded very much like a Scout Troop anywhere else. While she was talking, Sally and Peggy had left their table and were standing beside us listening to her with their heads on one side, their expressions quizzical. When she finished speaking, Peggy said, "We're working on foreign countries, Mrs. Miller, and we'd like to know what country you're from."

Susan gave a whoop of laughter. "Mrs. Miller's from Philadelphia, darling, her accent is called Eastern, but she is very much an American, even more so than we are."

"Oh," Peggy's face fell, "would you please come over and

talk to our table, Mrs. Miller? Our Troop wants to hear you talk."

Emily's dimple flickered. "Not today, Peggy. We have some more business to attend to." She had been keeping an eye on the embryonic Patrols. Her voice rose, "Have you chosen your names? Okay. Bring them over here and then I'll tell you what to do next."

As each "Patrol" representative handed her a name, she said, "Oak! That's a neat name. Maple—Alder—Fir—Pine—Cedar. Gosh! How'd you ever think up such neat names?"

She walked up to the head of the fourth-grade table and stood tall and erect, her eyes serene and sure. "Will 'Oak Patrol' please go upstairs and make us some gingerbread for our treat?"

Six "Tenderfeet" arose and filed past us, saying, "Please excuse me," and went upstairs to the kitchen, followed by Judy.

My chest swelled with pride as Emily said, "Will Maple and Alder please form in line and go up on the back porch and start planting their spring seeds?" Twelve third graders rose and proudly followed Jody out of the room.

Emily said, "That leaves Cedar and Pine and Fir." She came down to the table by us, where the new Brownies and the second graders were sitting, as good as pies, waiting to be told what to do. In front of them was their sand garden, a large flat enamel pan in which were embedded treasures we had gathered on our walks. Emily picked up one priceless possession after another. "Where did you find this rock with seaweed on it? It looks just like a little palm tree. On the beach, Kaziko? I never find things like that on the beach." She picked up Diana's notebook. "Did you paint all these bugs yourself, Diana? They're beautiful." Seashells, animals, leaves, flowers, around the table she went, admiring and exclaiming, but most remarkable, remembering each name. When she came to May's Nature notebook, each page scribbled with black crayola, she said. "May! Can you write Chinese?" May looked at her for a moment from beneath silken black lashes and said, "I can, but I didn't," and began to draw large Chinese characters in her notebook. Emily said, "Do you know what I think? I'll bet Pine and Fir will be the best Patrols of all when they get to be Scouts. Why don't you lend the new girls some of your nature pictures so they can get their notebooks started?"

"You can have this—do you want my rose?—do you want my crocodile?—" There was such a rush of cutting and pasting, they almost cut and pasted one another.

Emily grinned at me and went back to the first table and the six remaining "Tenderfeet." "Come on Cedar, let's write down the names in each 'Patrol' and see what suggestions you have to make. After all, you'll be using Patrols next year, and who knows, we might have to use this system every once in a while when we have joint meetings or field trips. Let's have a buzz on it." She sat down beside them and led a quiet, amicable discussion.

By this time, Susan and I were fairly bursting with pride and we both smiled fatuously at Mrs. Miller when she said, "My, but you are fortunate to have Senior Scouts helping you. Emily is an amazing girl, isn't she?"

We bragged about Emily and told Mrs. Miller about the biggest Community Christmas tree in the whole U-nited States and then asked her if she'd like to see our exhibits.

As we walked slowly around the bookcases, examining the Sit Upons, two pieces of oil cloth sewed together but very necessary to keep panties dry when sitting on wet grass, the paddle-board with nails in it to hold various colored threads, the straight board with jar lids screwed down on it to hold different sized nails, the needle cases in the shape of sunbonnet girls, made of felt with flannel squares to keep the needles from rusting, Mrs. Miller said, "Your crafts are ingenious. Your training program must have been excellent."

"We've just started Training Classes," I said, "it's Susan—she's a walking How-To-Do Book."

Mrs. Miller frowned slightly. "Surely you didn't start a Brownie Troop without taking the Training courses—"

"That we did," Susan grinned. "Actually we took over another Leader's Troop, but, like the old lady who lived in the shoe, when we found we had so many Brownies we didn't know what to do, we signed up for the Training courses."

"You'll find that your trainer recommends holding most of your meetings out of doors," Mrs. Miller said.

Susan's face stiffened into her "interfering mothers" expression, so I hastily explained that it rained nine months of the year here so we held most of our meetings indoors.

"That must tax your ingenuity—" Mrs. Miller began, and Susan interrupted, "It does, but we love it, and we have the biggest, if not the best, Brownie Troop in the whole U-nited States."

Mrs. Miller admired and understood our "collections." The box of named minerals Jim had produced when he was stumped by being asked to identify rocks; the dish gardens in oblong salmon tins, with their tiny lichens and minuscule plants and ferns, which I explained were largely produced by Sumiko and Kaziko who not only had gifted fingers but were willing to spend hours and hours helping the less imaginative children.

Mrs. Miller shook her head. "How fortunate you are to have an interracial Troop. We had difficulty squeezing in our weekly meetings, what with skating, music lessons, dancing, theatre, concerts, movies and TV. Children are so busy today and yet they *need* a play group." Again Susan was beaming, and said she thought we actually had more fun making the sample crafts than the children did.

When we got around to the animals, Mrs. Miller won Heidi's undying admiration by saying, "My, you're lucky, Heidi. In summer you can move your guinea pigs and rabbits around on the lawn. Much more fun than pushing a lawn mower. If you leave the radio on when you go to school, your parakeet will learn to talk more quickly." Judging by Heidi's expression, she was ready to pack up her animals and move in with the Millers.

Mrs. Miller knelt down and brought her eyes to Heidi's eye level. "Heidi? Have you ever been to the zoo in the spring when the animals have their new babies?"

Heidi said, "No! What's it like?"

"In Philadelphia, where we come from, we have a great big zoo. In the spring we go every single Saturday. We watch the mother seal teach her baby to swim by pushing him into the water and spanking him with her flippers when he tries to crawl out."

Heidi said, "Tell me some more."

By this time Pine and Fir had also left the table and were gathered around Mrs. Miller, panting to hear about zoo babies.

"—and the mother kangaroo hops around with her baby peeking out of her pouch, and the mother monkey swings through the branches with her baby tucked under her arm. We'll just have to take trips to the zoo in the spring to be sure we don't miss a single new baby."

"Will you take us? Will you take us?" they begged.

I experienced my first twinge of jealousy. *I* wanted to see Heidi watch the zoo babies. I said, "We'll all go. We'll go on Saturdays so we'll have lots of time."

Susan said, "Come on. There'll be repercussions if we don't show Mrs. Miller what the other 'Patrols' are doing."

We left Emily and Cedar guarding Pine and Fir and went upstairs to see how Oak was doing with the gingerbread. The kitchen smelled spicy and delicious, every utensil was washed and put away, the surfaces were gleaming, and Oak was sitting at the kitchen table poring over recipe books, supervised by Judy.

We admired their industry and went out onto the porch to see how Jody was getting along with Maple and Alder.

Their planting display was truly impressive. Each egg carton was marked on the inside like a Whitman Sampler with the name of the owner, the type of seed in each section and the date of planting.

Jody said, "Say, what are we going to do when these are ready to transplant? Some of the girls live in apartments and don't have gardens."

No doubt prompted by Mrs. Miller's zoo promises, I pointed grandly toward September's envisioned begonia bed, an area forty feet long by five feet wide, and said, "We'll plant them right over there. We'll divide that bed up into garden patches, surround each patch with stones, and paint your names on the stones with nail polish. How's that?"

Jody bit her lips. "Yeh, but what about Oak and Cedar and Pine and Fir? Where'll they plant theirs?" This time I swept the whole side yard with a gesture. "Wherever they like. As long as they don't dig up the shrubs, they can choose their own gardens."

"Are we going to transplant on Saturdays, also?" Susan murmured.

"Um-hum. Saturdays and Sundays," I said. "Why?"

"May I remind you that there are only seven days in a week? Monday we have my Troop, Wednesday we have your Troop, Friday we have Training Class, Saturday we take trips to the zoo, and Sunday we plant. Do you, by any chance, think Jim and Charlie are going to go for this?"

I shrugged. "They won't care as long as we don't Lead while they're home. What is it, Sally?" Sally and Peggy were plucking at my skirt and asking when they were going to give their Leader Play.

I suggested that they run downstairs and ask Emily. They came tearing back and said that Emily said as soon as the gingerbread was cooked, we'd all come up on the porch and eat hot gingerbread and watch the Leader Play. She also said for the seedplanters to come downstairs so they could rehearse.

Judy warned Maple and Alder not to forget to water their seeds and led them off the porch and down the outside entrance to the basement.

After they left, Helen Miller (by this time we were so cozy we were Helen, Susan and Mary) asked, "Do you do this all alone? Haven't you got a Troop Committee?"

Susan smiled. "I might just as well confess all. I'm an ex-playground instructor and therefore do not care for interfering mothers. Several times Mary has suggested that we use mothers, but I've voted against it. I still bear scars as the result of well-meaning mothers."

Helen Miller said, "Oh I don't agree with you at all. We found that discussion meetings with the mothers brought results far beyond those we anticipated."

I laughed, said indeed they did, and gave an acid description of our first mothers' meeting.

Helen didn't even smile but launched into a fervent defense of monthly mothers' meetings and how important the discussion of specific immaturity and its variations was to the perceptive parent as well as to the Leader.

Susan said briefly, "Mrs. Bean, our Troop Committee chairman, is going to hold a mothers' meeting once a month. You can go and tell us what they said."

There was a momentary silence which Helen broke. "By the way, I asked Bill to pick me up here on his way home. I hope you don't mind. Bill is just as interested in the children's activities away from home as I am."

Susan said Jim and Charlie were coming too, for the same reason.

Emily was standing behind Mrs. Miller during this interchange of pleasantries, waiting to speak to us. She said, "I hate to interrupt, but would you mind going into the house and waiting until we call you? We have to arrange the audience and the scenery." She handed Susan the Troop records. "I thought you might need these to show to Mrs. Miller." As Susan followed Mrs. Miller in the door, Emily murmured, "Handbook Happy, isn't she?" and ran back downstairs.

By five o'clock Mrs. Miller had given our Troop records a going over which made the Troop Committee's grilling seem mild, but she had also offered to take over the fourth-graders if she could meet in our gameroom until her furniture came. "I'd be better with them, I think, because I've been a Scout Leader for the last few years." This solution to our problem was obviously so practical that Susan didn't even rebel at Helen's cavalier appropriation of her Troop, but she did say we'd have to discuss it with our Brownies. I didn't have a chance to say anything, because Jim and Charlie and Bill Miller arrived just at that point to see the Leader's Play.

Emily came in and called us, and when we arrived on the porch, there were two rows of Brownies sitting on Sit Upons, and six chairs for us. The battered screen was wavering at the far end of the porch.

We sat down, Heidi passed us some hot gingerbread, and Durdey came out from behind the screen, crumbs ringing her mouth.

"I'm the announther. I wish to announth The Lonely Lady. It ith a play written by Thally Jay and Peggy Blake." She bowed and pulled back the screen.

"ACT I."

Sally is lying on one of the benches draped like a bed. She is wearing my best nylon nightgown, over her uniform, and my glasses, and she is propped up, chewing gingerbread and reading.

SALLY: Oh dear. I am so lonely. My house is dirty. My dishes are not done. My beds are not made. Everything is a mess. Who shall I call up?

She picks up a toy telephone, dials and says:

Hello, Susan. I'm nearly crazy, I have so much to do. I wish I had some children.

A Brownie pops up from behind her.

SALLY: Who are you?
BROWNIE: I am a Brownie. Why are you lonely?
SALLY: Because I am alone.
BROWNIE: Where are your children?
SALLY: (Beginning to sob) I have no children.
BROWNIE: Where is your husband?
SALLY: He is at a medical meeting. Boo-hoo-hoo.

Durdey pulled back the screen. "End of Act I."

Jim leaned forward and whispered to me, "You wrote this play."

"ACT II."

This time Sally is sleeping with a seraphic smile on her face, her glasses still in place. Two Brownies pop up.

PEGGY: Oh look. She is dreaming about children. Let us surprise her. Come, Brownies, come and help the Lonely Lady.

Brownies appear from behind chairs, planting boxes, bushes, under the table and pour out the door, and begin to sweep, do the dishes, make the beds, with many unflattering comments about the dirty, filthy house.

SALLY: (Yawning widely and sitting up) My, my, the house is clean. Who knows where I can get another husband and some children?
BROWNIES: I do, I do, I do, I do, I do, I do.
SALLY: Very well, get busy.

They all thunder offstage leaving the Lonely Lady to lie back and resume her peaceful sleep.

Durdey pulled back the screen. "End of Act II."

Jim and Charlie and Susan and Bill and Helen Miller were quietly having hysterics.

"Act III."

Patty, in Jim's hat and sport coat, sneaks onstage, looks suspiciously around, and leans over and kisses the Lonely Lady.

HUSBAND: Wake up. Wake up. I am your husband.

SALLY: (Sitting up and frowning) But you're the same old husband. They said they were going to get me a new one. I wonder who did all my housework. It must have been the Brownies.

THE TROOP: (Thundering on again) We are your children. (They begin to sing.) We have tidied everything, everything, everything. We have tidied everything, we are Brownies! (They melt away.)

When they had all disappeared and the stage was bare, Durdey came out from behind the screen. "Now can I have thome more gingerbread? Thith ith the end."

15

A GIRL SCOUT IS CHEERFUL

*I*T was the end of March. Susan and I had completed our Training Course and had gained sufficient self-confidence to house three Brownie Troops running full blast. On Monday afternoon, Helen Miller was the Leader of the "Tenderfeet" assisted by Jody. We attended the first couple of meetings, secretly hoping that she wasn't as efficient as she sounded, and then let her strictly alone, because her Troop obviously adored her, was even more Handbook Happy than she was, and Jody was developing a noticeable Philadelphia accent. Wednesday afternoon Susan led the third graders who were becoming neat, bossy, and putting out shoots of Sweet Reason now and then. She was assisted by Judy who admired her to such an extent that she had changed her college major to Physical Education so she could be "just like Mrs. Blake." I attended most of Susan's meetings to try to whet my appetite for games. Friday afternoon, Emily assisted me, or to be truthful, I assisted Emily in corralling the leftovers, the new ones, the little sisters, and the nonconformists, Diana and May, and Heidi who impartially attended all meetings.

All week long the house boiled with Brownies. This was

219

Field Trip Day, or what we had come to regard as a normal Saturday morning.

Jim didn't have to start making hospital rounds until nine o'clock. I had already fed the children and the ones who'd stayed-all-night, and was cooking our breakfast while Jim read the paper and drank coffee.

Meanwhile Heidi was waiting for my Troop who arrived one at a time, banged open the door, said, "G'morning, Doctor Jay. Come on, Heidi," and clumped down the basement stairs to foregather for a trip to the zoo with Helen Miller.

As they passed, Jim chanted, "Good morning. Close the door, please."

As each one said, "G'morning" to me, I checked her name off on the Troop list thumbtacked to the cupboard over the stove and chanted, "Good morning. Close the basement door, please" and continued to broil veal kidneys and bacon.

The house rang with peals of laughter and sounds of scuffling from Susan's Troop, who had foregathered on the side porch with Sally, waiting to go on a Cookout.

Jim held out his cup for more coffee. "Surely there are more. Where is Mari's Troop?"

"They're coming later to make plans for Dad's night. You'll be home early, won't you?" I put the platter of kidneys and bacon in front of him as a peace offering.

His face lighted up at the kidneys, but his voice still held an aggrieved note. "I thought we were going shopping this afternoon."

I laughed and said we were. "This is a cooking project and Helen asked me to take her Troop. She's going to have her Troop meetings at her house if her furniture ever comes." Jim snorted, and I added hastily, "I do hope you can make it for Dad's night. Mari is chairman, and Oak and Cedar are going to cook dinner all by themselves, real Italian spaghetti, garlic bread, green salad and hot apple pie."

Jim grinned. "Firstborn certainly has become self-reliant, hasn't she? I'll be there. When is it?"

I said next Saturday night, and I'd offered our dining room and living room in honor of the occasion.

"That means dear Phyllis will spend the week end again." Jim groaned. "Would it be churlish of me to add that I'm getting just a wee bit tired of dear Phyllis?"

There were sounds of altercation from the living room, followed by Phyllis' flat voice, "Mymother always uses canned spaghetti and canned meatballs!" (Sweet Reason seemed to have fled from Helen Miller's rigid Leadership.)

Mari's voice was coming nearer. "We wouldn't dare use canned spaghetti. My father wouldn't even touch one bite. Mo-ther-r-r!"

Their red faces appeared at the kitchen door. "You wouldn't even touch one bite of canned spaghetti, would you, Daddy?"

Jim shook his head. "I'd starve first."

I told them to go back to the living room and make a written menu and a list of fathers, and I'd be there as soon as I finished breakfast.

Emily stuck her head in the back door. "Mrs. Jay? Oh excuse me, Doctor Jay. I thought you'd gone."

Jim sighed and I asked Emily what she wanted.

"The D.T.'s are supposed to give a basket social for the Kings tonight. Judy and Jody and I were just wondering if you had any good ideas for our basket lunches. But you're busy, we'll talk to you after the Field Trip. Shall we check the 'Patrols?' " I nodded and the back door slammed.

"Mo-ther-r-r?" Heidi's voice floated up the basement stairs. "Will you call Helen's mother? She said she'd be here by nine and it's almost nine. Will you, Mother?"

I asked Jim to excuse me, called Helen Miller to find she'd already left, and came back to breakfast.

Jim asked, "When do *I* get a turn with you?"

I said I'd be through by noon and could go shopping any time after that. "Why don't you come home for lunch?" I asked.

"I might do that, if you'll guarantee the Brownies will be gone." He leaned down and kissed me. "Good-bye, little mother of all living. Don't forget we're going fishing tomorrow."

"I won't." I followed him out to the car to find a regular traffic jam in front of the house. The driving mothers, plus the dropping-off mothers, had arrived.

With a hasty " 'Bye darling. See you at lunch," I took the various Troop lists out of my pocket and began to check them off, thinking as I did so, what a godsend Emily's so-called Patrols were on a day like this. Bunches of six were so much easier to keep track of than thirty-six stragglers. Susan's Troop had two station wagons. My Troop had two cars and one station wagon—three zoo mothers. Helen's Troop would be dropped off to plan their menu with me, and picked up again after they were through with their Dad's night meeting. Since Mrs. Bean had organized our Field Day mothers, Saturdays were a cinch.

Gaily running from car to car, I invited the mothers in for a cup of coffee and additional briefing for the coming ordeals.

Susan said, "Take their license numbers too. Then we can call a prowler car when they fail to show to pick up their loved ones."

We sat down at the kitchen table and tried to make ourselves heard over the din of banging doors, shrieks of greeting and loud, bossy orders. "See that they use the Buddy system, make them report to you at half-hour intervals—see that they understand the time they are to meet to go home—show them the clock—" I repeated.

"I just don't see how you stand this week after week,"

Mrs. Allen said, "Honestly! I think you are just wonderful—"

Susan said, "We are." I said hastily that it wasn't wonderful at all. It just took planning and organization and a mania for children.

"Don't forget bull strength and voice." Susan rose. "Come on. We might just as well gird up our loins and start cutting out the herd." She stretched. "To think that I used to wail because I only had one chick."

We went out to the front sidewalk where the children were seething and shoving. "Form your Patrols!" Susan roared. Instantly they coagulated into groups of six. She called off their names in a stentorian voice. "Oh dear, Diana and May are missing again. Do you suppose they'll ever learn to be on time?"

"Oh sure. At least they attend every meeting now—here they are—" Diana and May, hand in hand, were wandering toward us, giggling foolishly.

Susan said, "-thirty-three-thirty-four-thirty-five-thirty-six. All here." By ten o'clock the sorted "Patrols" and their complement of driving mothers and Emily and Judy and Jody and I stood on the sidewalk waiting for Helen Miller.

"Mary?" There was a swivel of heads in the direction of the call.

I turned to see Edith Stokes, the President of the Neglected Ones (the only club I still made any pretense of attending), parking her long blue station wagon with its back to the curb.

"Edith!" I clapped my hands to my head and moaned. "The Garden Sale! I completely forgot it!"

Edith began to remove flats of chrysanthemums from the back of her station wagon. There was a surge of helpful Scouts toward her, and she impartially handed over flat after flat.

"What's the matter, Mrs. Jay? What's wrong?" Emily

shook my arm. "Gee, you look funny. What's the matter?"

"Nothing except that I'm chairman of the chrysanthemum section of the Garden Sale. I haven't been to a meeting since November, and I forgot all about it. This is the day we were supposed to transplant thousands of shoots. Oh, what *am* I going to do?"

There were calls of "Hey! Where do you want these? Is it all right to put these on the grass?"

I was too appalled to answer. Emily took over. "Just line them up in the side yard." She left me and went to supervise.

Organized and planned, was I? I was supposed to have called the entire roster of the Neglected Ones and beaten on them until I had at least ten however reluctant volunteers. I had not even called Edith. And at the November meeting I'd tried Phyllis' technique and stormed that if they weren't willing to volunteer, I was much too busy with the Brownies to be chairman!

Emily pulled at my arm. "What'll I tell Mrs. Stokes? What were you supposed to do?"

"Never mind, Emily. It's a little complicated. I'll have to talk to her."

Edith handed out the last flat and came over to me. "Now, Mary. These chrysanthemums are in prime condition. Be sure to wet them down before you begin to transplant them. They are all labeled, so don't get them mixed up. These are the best we've ever had, all spider or spoon. We should get at least fifty cents a plant for them, and that flat of Nightingales will bring a dollar if you handle them carefully. We should clear at least two hundred dollars. I'm sorry I can't stay to help you, but I promised to go up to the Diabetic Camp today. What time are your volunteers coming?"

I just looked at her.

"Now, Mary. You'll have to start transplanting them right

away. They're all named varieties and I had an awful time persuading the growers to give them up."

I nodded, and she walked briskly over to her station wagon and drove off, leaving me numb with horror at my muddle-headedness.

Emily said, "Do you have to transplant every one of those little shoots? I've helped Mother do that, and boy, what a job!"

I said yes and it would take hours and hours because I had forgotten to call the other doctors' wives who were supposed to help me.

A warm arm hugged me, and Emily shouted, "Hey, Patrols! Mrs. Jay forgot again. She needs help. Who wants to help her?"

I found myself surrounded by waving arms and eager faces. "What do you want us to do?"

Emily said, "A Girl Scout's duty is to be cheerful and useful and help others, remember? We have to help her transplant all these plants for the Children's Hospital Garden Sale."

"What about Dad's night and the Cookout and the zoo?" Phyllis asked.

Emily laughed. "What about it? We'll have a great big planting party, and Judy and Jody and I'll help."

Mrs. Allen said, "If I'd known I didn't have to drive, I could have been home ironing. Honestly, this Brownie business."

I started to apologize, but Susan advanced toward her. "We have ironing too, Mrs. Allen. I have three baskets at home right this minute—"

Mrs. Allen backed away. "I didn't mean it like that. It's just that ever since Darleen's been a Brownie, it seems as if all I've done is drive—" her voice faded before Susan's glare.

"Of course if you'd rather not have Darleen in the Troop—"

"Mo-ther-r-r," Darleen wailed.

Feeling distinctly guilty, I asked if some of the Troop members wouldn't rather go on with their plans.

Emily called, "Who wants to go on with their plans?"

Not one hand was raised, so Mrs. Allen and the other somewhat ruffled mothers got into their cars and drove away.

I turned to Susan. "I feel like such a fool. Sounding off about being so well planned and organized, and now this. I feel just awful."

"I don't. It's good for them to find out what we've been going through. Mothers! Let's get started."

Helen Miller came panting up. "So sorry. I had to find something for Bill. Where's our transportation?"

I sheepishly explained my idiotic predicament and Emily's solution.

Helen shrugged. "What difference does it make? Rooting cuttings is part of our Agricultural Project. Come on, let's get started. Isn't this a heavenly day?"

I led the children toward the side yard, fervently thanking God for several blessings. The spring wind had blown the grass fairly dry, and the pale sun was almost warm. Fortunately, in a fit of self-righteous indignation after I had come home from the last Garden Sale Meeting, I had ordered the river sand, loam, peat moss, plant bands, labels, hormone powder, and flats, and they were all stacked under the back porch.

I turned to the children. "Sit down on the porch steps and the wall, and I'll show you how to transplant a chrysanthemum shoot. Then you tell me how you think we can do it the best and the fastest."

I gathered the necessary materials, picked up a clump of Edith's cherished Nightingale, removed a fragile green shoot, and thought, "This will never work. How can I expect children to transplant and label the shoots correctly when grown women lost about twenty-five per cent of them last year?"

I mixed the soil, filled the plant band, dipped the shoot in water and then in hormone powder, and planted it. Then I wrote "Nightingale—spoon—late bloomer" on the label and put it down for inspection.

The "Patrols" lined up and filed past. The word "bloomer" caused a few giggles, but they examined the dirt and the shoot and the rest of the clump with great interest.

When they had all filed past, Emily said, "It's a cinch. We can transplant these in nothing flat."

Jody said, "Mrs. Jay? We did a Christmas Seal project once that was kind of like this. Each Patrol had a special job. One folded, one filled envelopes, one licked, and one stamped. We had more darn fun!"

One very small Pine needle raised her hand. "Say, what is a ker-cruh-kersantheum, anyway?"

Susan said, "That's a good question. I was just going to ask it myself," went down to the gameroom and came back with our garden books and seed catalogs. We spent half an hour matching labels to pictures which, as Susan remarked acidly, would be a lot easier if each grower had not felt called upon to be original both in naming and describing the varieties.

Judy said, "You know what? I think we should put the color on the labels. Some people might think a Nightingale is a bird. I did."

"I still do," Susan muttered. "Any other ideas, girls?"

While I sorted the clumps, pulled the shoots off and put them on separate sheets of labeled paper, Helen and her Troop got the work tables and benches out of the gameroom and brought them up on the terrace. Then we set my Troop to sifting sand and filling buckets, while Susan's Troop took turns carrying one bucket of peat moss, one bucket of loam, and one bucket of sand and dumping it in the wheelbarrow. Then Helen's Troop made plant bands and filled them, Emily and Judy and Jody wrote labels, and Susan and Helen and I transplanted and stacked the plants in flats.

By noon we were all covered with mud and having a whee of a time, when Peggy took hold of my arm. "Shouldn't we start the fire if we're going to have our Cookout here?"

Susan shook her head. "Takes too long to cook Campstew." She turned to me. "What do you say if we use our Troop funds to buy some hamburger? The treasuries are loaded."

Jane and Sally began to moan, "Can't we use something we already have?" Phyllis and Mari yelled, "Dibbies to do the cooking. Who wants to help cook?"

For the first time since we'd been Leaders, it seemed that all Brownies would rather transplant chrysanthemums than cook.

Just at that moment, Jim came around the corner of the house calling, "Anybody home? Any lunch?" He took one look at the grimy gardeners and burst out laughing. "I wish you could see your faces. You look as if you'd been down in a coal mine. What on earth are you doing?"

The Oaks and Cedars began a lecture on the care and transplanting of chrysanthemum shoots and were interrupted constantly by the Maples and Alders who wished to start building the outdoor fire, and the Pines and Firs who wished food. They were hungry.

He said, "Just a minute. Hold on a minute," and stood watching our assembly line, his eyes crinkling with laughter. "Everybody seems to have a job but me. Why don't I cook lunch?"

His own loyal offspring gave derisive shouts. "D-a-a-d-dy! You can't cook. Da-a-addy! We even have to make your pumpernickel sanrishes. Da-a-addy! You can't even tell if it's plain milk or buttermilk till you taste it."

Goaded by these jeers, Daddy said, "I'll show you who's a Boy Scout," and disappeared.

Soon he was back with large cartons of provender. I went in to see what Boy Scouts have for lunch and found tremendous quantities of wienies, pickles, ice cream cones, ice cream, two cases of hideously colored pop, and two packages of pancake mix.

Phyllis and Mari came in and looked over this lavish display. Mari asked, "How are you going to cook pancakes outdoors?" and Phyllis clucked, "There aren't many vitamins here. It is not enough to be able to prepare and serve a meal well. You must also know something about the nutritional needs of your family. Do you know the meaning of proteins, carbohydrates, fats and vitamins?"

Jim looked down at his incubus. "Phyllis, I'm going to risk a curbstone consultation. You look to me as if you were afflicted with incipient excess obesity. If I were you, I'd just sit over there in the corner and gnaw on a carrot while the rest of us make flapjacks."

"Jim! Not flapjacks—" I wailed.

He nodded. "Every Western girl should know how to make flapjacks, and flapjacks we are going to have."

Phyllis' lips were moving as she stared at Jim through her round glasses. "Doctor Jay, my incipient excess obesity is because I am ten years old and am beginning to mature, *not* because I have a vitamin deficiency."

Jim blinked. "Phyllis, you constantly amaze me. Perhaps you'd better help me cook lunch, otherwise I doubt if I'd be successful."

While Susan and I finished transplanting the last of the chrysanthemums, Helen gathered her Troop around her to explain the delights of Backyard Camping. Taking a jack-knife out of her pocket, she showed them how to make fuzz sticks. Jim laid the fire in the firepit, the whole Troop directing. "Don't roll your newspaper, it'll just smoke. Use fuzz sticks. Girl Scouts use fuzz sticks." He started to put a wienie on a toasting fork, and Phyllis snatched at it. "You have to boil them first. Wienies contain pork, and pork might contain trichinosis. You have to boil them first." They took the pickles away from him and put them on paper plates, "Scouts don't wash unnecessary dishes," put straws in the pop bottles, "Scouts don't waste paper cups," and asked permission to make carrot and celery sticks because Scouts require vitamins.

Helen smiled fondly on them, but Jim stopped beside me. "This is the first time I ever fully appreciated the extent of your sterling qualities. Woman—you have the patience of a saint."

Phyllis, who was sticking to Jim like a burr, also stopped and listened to this pretty compliment with her head on one side. "No, Doctor Jay, she is *not* patient. She is when she's cooking or gardening or doing something she likes to do, but you should see her when she is trying to do crafts. Mrs. Blake had to help us with all of our crafts. Why, one time she—"

Jim put his hand over her mouth. "As I was saying, Griselda, how about dinner and a show tonight?"

By one-thirty we were sitting around the firepit, flipping the last of the flapjacks into the air. The terrace was dotted with flapjacks and dogs, the Brownies were saying, "Boy! Flapjacks are good. I'm going to teach my father how to make flapjacks!" and Emily and Judy and Jody were enlivening this Western scene with dull tales of "steadies" and "He saids and she saids" which made Susan and Helen and me shudder for the future, but which the Brownies listened to in openmouthed worship.

Jim was gazing into the fire with a slight frown on his face. During the screamingly funny denouement of one of these dreary sagas, Jim murmured, " 'Phyllis says' seems brilliant compared to these—"

Emily gave Jim a dark blue, melting look. "I'll bet you don't like to hear about dates and stuff, it makes you feel old. Say, you were an Eagle Scout, weren't you? Tell us some of the dangerous things you used to do."

Jim gave a medical facsimile of the grocery boy's exploits, heavily accenting sunburn, poison ivy, sprained ankles and broken legs, while Emily and Judy and Jody leaned their chins on their palms, batted their eyelashes at him, and said, "Doctors *sure are interesting!*"

When this game had palled, Emily suggested that we play "Who Am I" which had infinite variations and had proved to be equally fascinating to all three Troops.

Emily stood up and held her fingers to her eyes like glasses. "Girls. Your attention, please. This is a shrimp. A shrimp is a crustacean which inhabits these waters. It has a long body, slender legs and a depressed abdomen—"

"Don'ty Dale!" shrieked the Seniors.

Susan and I tried to look disapproving, but Emily looked and sounded so exactly like Miss Dale that it was difficult to keep a straight face.

"My turn—my turn!" Sally frowned earnestly at Peggy who was sitting next to her. "Now girls, Daddy is tired. Please don't bicker. When Daddy comes home, he is tired and I want you to be pleasant. It isn't that Daddy minds talking, he wants you to talk, it's just that he dislikes bickering. Daddy works so hard and when he comes home, he like to have a pleasant atmosphere. That's why I'm asking you not to bicker—"

I was the only one present who didn't think Sally was killingly funny.

Peggy got up. "Hey you guys—" she sucked in her cheeks and frowned. "Mothers! Honestly—"

Hastily interrupting, I said that Scouts were loyal. They

always removed the beams from their own eyes before they removed the motes from their friends' eyes. Which, of course, turned into, "What is a mote? What is a beam? How did you get it in your eye? How do you get it out?"

I stood up and, as a punishment to Susan and Helen and Jim for joining in the laughter at Sally's too good imitation of me, left them to struggle out of this straitjacket while I went in to call the mothers who were to retrieve Maple and Alder and Pine and Fir. True to Susan's prediction, two of them weren't home. I came out on the porch to ask Helen if she'd mind taking our station wagon and delivering them and heard Helen say to Susan—

"—but Mary doesn't pay enough attention to procedure. She allows them to do exactly as they please. Diana wanders in and out of the Troop meetings at will, and as for May Chinn—just look at them—"

May and Diana and Heidi were cooking flapjacks. That is, they were giggling and cooking little dime-sized pellets and tossing them to the dogs who were gulping and then looking bewildered because they couldn't taste anything.

Susan laughed indulgently. "They're just being themselves and so is Mary. Don't forget, she was the only woman in that Training Class who had never been a Campfire Girl or a Girl Scout. She took to the training class like a duck to water, but I will admit I nearly had hysterics when we were playing Hound and Hare. All she did was huddle under a tree like a scared rabbit and beg me not to chase her. I'll help her with Games until she loses her self-consciousness—" she looked up and saw me standing in the doorway. "How many of the dear mothers have forgotten that they ever had children?"

"Two." I asked Helen if she'd mind driving the rest.

"Not at all. I think we ought to send them home now so you can spend some time with Doctor Jay." She stood up. "My, we've certainly had a pleasant Backyard Camping experience. I'll Lead them in some Campfire songs while they're waiting for Transportation."

After they had all gone, Jim was so exhausted he had to take a nap to recuperate from being a Boy Scout. Susan offered to supervise the Dad's night supper plans, while I helped Emily and Judy and Jody plan and execute a brilliantly original basket lunch for hungry males. Gallons of milk, chocolate cake, pickles, stuffed eggs, tuna fish sandwiches and fruit, for which they provided the materials.

"Say, Emily, I've got three chickens in the icebox. Why don't I fry them for you while you are making the cake?" I asked.

"Oh no. We couldn't ask you to do that. Gee, you're always so darned nice to us, but Stan sure loves fried chicken."

I assured her that three fried chickens could never make up for three busy, popular Senior Scouts who were willing to give up one precious afternoon a week and every Saturday morning to be Program Aides.

They looked genuinely astonished.

Emily also came over to our house to sleep after the basket social so Jim and I could leave at four o'clock Sunday morning and spend a pleasant and restful day on the Sound recuperating and casting for the elusive cutthroat trout.

Monday morning Susan called at eight-thirty to report the repercussions from the planting party and to chide me for cravenly sneaking off with Jim, leaving her to deal with "mothers!"

Two Firs were green as a result of Jim's flapjacks. A doctor should know better than to feed children all that stuff. One Maple had reported that they didn't go on their Cookout. They had to stay home and work and plant a whole lot of flowers which Mrs. Jay was going to sell on account of they were so poor. Perhaps it would be advisable to call Maple's mother. A new mother wanted to know why

Eloise had gotten so dirty and why she hadn't gone to the zoo. She was anxious to have Eloise go to the zoo to see the baby animals. "That, from an animal who has a white stripe clear down her back," Susan fumed.

"Did they call Helen Miller too?" I asked.

"Um-hum. She spent all day Sunday explaining why several small Pines were pale around the gills. We talked it over and decided that it must have been the purple pop rather than the flapjacks, or maybe it was a combination of the two."

I promised I would call the mothers listed and pacify each one with a few well-turned phrases from the Training Class.

It was noon before I had a chance to call Edith Stokes and ask her to come over and pass on the chrysanthemums. She said she would drop by at one-thirty on the way to the Medical Auxiliary Board Meeting. I hadn't had a chance to do more than make the beds and rinse the breakfast dishes, so I whizzed around stuffing things in drawers, whisking off surfaces and straightening books and magazines in a feeble attempt to reassure that doctor's wife that this doctor's wife always kept Jim's house surgically clean.

I might have known it wouldn't work. The first thing Edith said was, "Now Mary, I'm afraid your Girl Scout activities are taking up too much of your time. A doctor should have his wife's undivided attention. His home is his castle and it should be clean and quiet and restful at all times."

Counting to ten, and then to twenty, I took Edith out on the porch to show her the chrysanthemums sitting in row on row of neatly labeled flats and told her proudly that Brownies and Scouts had transplanted them all.

"Now Mary. They look all right, but you really shouldn't have allowed little children to do that. It is the duty of every doctor's wife to help the hospitals. Now you have wasted at least ten potential volunteer doctors' wives by allowing children to transplant these chrysanthemums. I hope enough of them survive to make something at our booth, but I doubt it. Chrysanthemums are hardy, but children, in my experience, are never reliable."

Then and there I determined to bring every single plant through if I had to bring my pallet down and sleep by the blasted things all night.

Chrysanthemums are hardy, all right. Ours were so robust they withstood the sprinkling cans and loving care of Helen's whole Troop who welcomed this opportunity to practice Agriculture. They not only grew, they flourished. Susan and Helen and I were so proud of them we asked Mrs. Bean to provide sufficient transportation to drive every Oak, Cedar, Maple, Alder, Pine and Fir to the Children's Hospital Garden Sale so they could bask in the admiration of the Neglected Ones. I'd show Edith Stokes what Brownie Scouts could do!

Mrs. Bean was so enthusiastic about this community service, she provided a whole fleet of cars. The Troops all wore their Brownie uniforms that day, were picked up after school and driven downtown to the sale. By the time they arrived, their sturdy chrysanthemums had been sold and had brought in over three hundred and twenty-five dollars.

Edith Stokes was loud in her praises of "those remarkable Girl Scouts" and called the Neglected Ones over to meet our Troops and thank them individually for their amazing gardening ability, and to explain to them that this money was going to help little children who were sick.

We were soon surrounded by admiring doctors' wives. From all sides came paeans of praise. "Aren't they darling? Just imagine giving up one whole Saturday to plant, and then remembering to *water* the plants. I wish I had some Brownies to help me. Aren't they *darling?*"

Phyllis was explaining how we organized our Troops into

"Patrols" and each "Patrol" did a special job while Helen and Susan and I beamed at her. During the "oh's" and "ah's" of admiration and interest at her intelligent explanation, she said to me in a loud penetrating whisper, "What's the matter with all these women? Don't they know we're supposed to help other people?"

16

FLYING UP

*I*T was really spring. The forget-me-nots bloomed under the rows of pink tulips, the sky was feathery with white clouds, and the trees transformed our streets into flower-decked aisles. The air was soft and balmy, our Brownies were ecstatic and wished to spend every possible moment frisking in the Out-of-Doors.

But the time had come for the ancient Oaks and Cedars to be thinned out. It was of prime importance that we have at least one joint meeting to talk over the all-important Flying Up Ceremony at which the ten-year-olds would graduate and turn into Intermediate Girl Scouts, and which would provide the occasion for that "great big party" I had rashly promised the Storm Troopers and mothers at Mrs. Bean's.

Mrs. Miller and Susan and I spent hours going over our lists and trying to decide whether to have a Flying Up tea and invite the mothers who could come, or to put faith in our unfaithful spring weather and give a great big family picnic in the Out-of-Doors.

Mrs. Miller was all for the family picnic. "Bill and the children and I would love it. It's so beautiful here. Surely by the end of May we can plan on nice weather."

Susan looked pityingly at her. "You don't know our Great White Father. The moment he suspects a family outing, he covers us in rain clouds. We can't trust the weather until after the Fourth of July." She looked just as pityingly at our living room. "And if it rains, there is no possible way we can stuff thirty-six Brownies, their parents and heaven knows how many honor guests and sisters and brothers into this house. Believe me, the walls would come tumbling down."

We argued and discussed and planned and finally decided to have another joint meeting and present both plans to our Troops and leave the decision up to them.

So, on the last Monday in April, we produced shrieks of rage and frustration by vetoing Helen's tree-identifying walk, Susan's Cookout in the Park, and my walk to "see the pretty flars," and had a joint meeting in the gameroom.

Even Helen's Troop, by this time reliable, responsible ten-year-olds, were sitting at their table with shadowed eyes and sullen mouths, grumbling. Susan's Troop, now nine-going-on-ten, were argumentative and saying, "Why-y-y-y-y?" My Troop, just barely able to sit still for fifteen minutes, were peering out the windows, visibly longing to go outdoors and play.

I stood up and said, "Will each Troop please take roll, collect your dues, and finish your formal meeting as soon as possible." Emily, Jody and Judy went to the tables to expedite matters.

"We'd better ask Mrs. Bean to call a mothers' meeting so we can explain the adult aspect of this entertainment," Helen Miller said.

Susan sighed. "I suppose we'd better, particularly if they decide to have the Great Big Family Picnic—"

When the tumult and the shouting had died down enough so we could hear ourselves think, I stood up and asked them how they would like to have a Flying Up tea party and invite their mothers to come.

There were protests from Oak and Cedar who didn't want to give a tea party. They'd served at P.T.A. teas at school, and they weren't any fun. Anyway, how could you invite mothers to a tea party when they didn't even get home until five-thirty? Maple and Alder said, "Yeah!" and "Gee whiz!" Pine and Fir twisted their heads back and forth like owlets, asking, "What is a T?"—"How do you give a T?"

I explained a Flying Up tea, open-faced sandwiches which they would make, cakes which their mothers would bring, songs which each Troop would sing, and the Flying Up Ceremony to which we would invite Miss Dale and Miss Smith from the Council.

Helen's Troop stood up and asked permission to go into the laundry room to have a "buzz." While they were gone, Emily explained to my Troop that a "T" was just like a treat only it was prettier and much more fun and their mothers would be all dressed up and—

Helen's Troop came marching back and announced that they didn't care for teas. Teas were in the afternoon when it was nice outdoors, eight of their mothers couldn't come because they worked, and it wasn't fair.

"Well then," I said, "how would you like to have a great big family picnic on the last Saturday in May down at the Park? We'll spend the rest of this meeting writing invitations to your mothers and fathers. But remember, we will have the picnic, IF it doesn't rain."

Rain or shine, they loved the picnic. Amid the hysterical gabble, Susan said, "When your house is bulging and it's pouring and raining, don't say you didn't ask for it."

I held up three fingers again, by now as effective as popping a cork in a seltzer bottle. "How would you like to spend the month of May completing your crafts so you can give them to your parents as presents?"

"Mine isn't finished yet." "What crafts?" "My mother already has a pot holder." "What'll I give my Dad?"

"Wouldn't this be simpler to handle at the separate Troop meetings?" Helen asked.

"We'll have to go over and over it, but the ones who were with Mrs. Burton last year still cling to the idea that they're one Troop indivisible—" I said as Emily and Judy and Jody began to walk up and down the long tables patting shoulders. "Relax. Relax. Scouts are courteous. One at a time. Everybody will have a present. Relax—"

"We will have the Flying Up Ceremony in the afternoon before the parents arrive—"

A barrage of questions. "How do you Fly Up? Up where?"

"Relax—relax. One at a time—"

Helen Miller clapped her hands over her ears. "How will we ever get anything decided?"

Susan grinned. "Just like any other gathering of females— by all talking at once." She patted Helen's shoulder. "Relax —relax—"

Emily walked to the head table. "Stand up, Oak and Cedar, and let the Brownies see what Brownie Scouts look like when they're ready to Fly Up and become Intermediates." As they stood, I realized that no longer were they tall, short, fat, thin, gangly and coltish. In one short year they had grown more uniform in size with slight bulges here and there and their manner was almost as calm and self-possessed as the Seniors. The Brownies and I stared at them in awe-stricken silence.

Emily sat down with them and I continued. "We will invite all of your mothers and fathers and play games and have a Cookout in the Out-of-Doors and show them how much fun we have and how dandy it is to be a Brownie Scout."

Colleen said, "My Mom can't come unless she brings my little brother." From all sides—"Can my little sister and brother come too?" "Can I bring my big sister?" "Can I bring my cousin?" "Can I bring my Aunt—"

Helen Miller sang, "—and your sisters and your cousins and you have 'em by the dozens and your a-a-a-aunts!"

Jane had bustled over to Peggy who was joined by May Chinn, our treasurer. "How much is all this going to cost?"

By the time we had finished comforting our accountants over the cost, explaining that we were all going to be in uniform, that we would meet at the Park at one o'clock to hold the Flying Up Ceremony, *before* the parents arrived, so Oak and Cedar would already be Intermediate Girl Scouts and could wear their green uniforms *when* their mothers and fathers got there, and Why-y-y-y-y-y, it was almost five-thirty.

We streamed out of the house to find three impatient mothers and one sullen father, drivers who had been waiting half an hour.

Helen Miller began going from car to car apologizing. "I'm so sorry you had to wait. We had a joint meeting and it took longer than we anticipated. I'm so sorry—"

"Oh, so am I," Susan muttered, "just crushed. Imagine having to spend half an hour waiting for a Brownie Troop. *I'm* sorrier that we didn't come out and get them and bring them downstairs so they would have a vague idea of what we go through Monday, Wednesday, Friday and Saturday for *their* little dears." She chuckled. "I can just hear Charlie —'Nobody makes you do this, Susan. You can stop any time you really want to.' Let's have our regular meetings Wednesday and Friday anyway, so we can explain the Flying Up Ceremony to ours. Let's both Lead both days, much simpler." She herded Peggy and her riders into her car and drove off.

Tuesday Pat Smith called. "How are you coming with your Camp applications?"

Helen Miller was handling the whole thing for us. She'd had years of experience and understood just how to take care of the requirements. "As far as we can tell now, the ones who need it most, like Minnie and Sumiko and Colleen, can't afford to go, and the ones who do not need it are all signed up."

Pat Smith said, "Ask Mrs. Miller to come down and talk it over with us. Now and then we can make arrangements for special cases. When are you going to have your Flying Up Ceremony?"

I told her about our proposed Great Big Family Picnic the last Saturday in May, asked her to extend our invitation to Miss Dale, and warned her to expect a formal invitation from all three Troops.

She laughed. "I'd very much like to come, and I'm sure Miss Dale would also. We're anxious to see those Troops in action."

The next Monday we began to have what amounted to daily meetings. By so doing we were able to complete their needle cases or spools of thread boards, or nail jar boards for Dad, or dish gardens for Mom and Dad, or candle boards or spoon holders or ashtrays or pot holders or pipe racks or toothbrush holders or tie racks, and *still* spend a part of each Monday, Wednesday and Friday taking brief walks so we could stand under a shower of pink cherry blossoms, or gather the first dandelions, or make forget-me-not bouquets for Mother.

Helen Miller, whose furniture had at long last arrived, held two or three dessert and coffee mothers' meetings at night, at which time she explained the Camp Registration and tried to get a rough idea of how many sisters and brothers and cousins and aunts we were to expect at our picnic, and I avoided explaining why we had not invited mothers to our meetings by saying that my husband was a physician, which had nothing to do with it but was received by nods of sympathy and understanding.

After these meetings, we had lunch together in the game-room and made lists of food and Park benches and tables and probable attendance.

"Even if we make cauldrons of Campstew," Helen reported, "do you realize we will have well over a hundred mouths to feed?"

"We have almost fifty dollars in our combined treasuries which must be spent by the end of the year. Pat told us so in the Training Course—" I said.

Susan laughed. "You sound like a Brownie—'My Mom says so'—"

Every afternoon the gameroom rang with furious activity reminiscent of our Christmas preparations. Helen's Troop took to coming to Susan's and my meetings to hold buzz sessions on the menu and made several trips up to Vi and Murph's to see if there was any form of food which would serve one hundred people at fifty cents a person.

Jane came back from these trips in deep mourning. "That man at the bank said we wouldn't get one cent of interest if we withdrew our Troop funds. Hamburger is expensive and so is bacon and so are potatoes and onions and carrots. Murph said he would give us everything wholesale, on account of it's a Community Project, but food costs so *darned much!* Why-y-y-y-y can't they bring their own nosebags?"

Sally gasped, "Did you know that ice cream costs ten dollars? Murph says we have to have *five gallons!*"

Jane threw a protective arm around Sally's shoulders, and they shook their heads over the high cost of living.

The week before the picnic, it poured rain which made the Troops nervous and irritable while they were finishing their crafts, but not half as nervous and irritable as it made their Leaders.

Emily kept dropping in to see me on the way home from school, counting chairs and couches, measuring the downstairs rooms with her eye, and saying, "Even if we feed the little kids out on the porch, how are we going to make Campstew for all those people?"

"Relax, Emily, relax," I said. "We can use the top of the stove and the oven and the auxiliary oven and Susan's stove and Helen's stove if we have to, but I don't think we have to. The weather man says it's going to be a lovely day."

"The weather man!" Emily sniffed. "He's ruined every single Class Day since I was a Freshman. Even if it isn't raining, the Park will be all sopping wet and the wood won't burn. If only we didn't have so many people." She gazed at me with her delphinium blue eyes. "Next year, *please* don't have so many Brownies. Honestly, you won't believe it, but if you had just one regular Brownie Troop and one meeting a week, you wouldn't have any trouble at all."

I promised, regretted that I had taken in every straggler who wanted to come, and finished with, "But Emily, if I had it to do over again, I'd do exactly the same thing. Too many children in this district need somewhere to play and someone to watch over them."

Emily hugged me. "You're great, you really are. Now listen, how many big kettles have you got? Mom has one and we're going to put bacon in the bottom and then a layer of sliced potatoes and then a layer of hamburger and onions and then a layer of carrots, and so on up to the top. And have great big bowls of green salad and then ice cream and Gloria's mother is going to furnish all the cake we want, free. I said she could because she feels so badly because you're so nice to Gloria and she can't help you more." She looked down at her hands and was silent for a moment.

"Would it hurt your feelings if I told you something?" she asked. "Promise?"

I promised not to allow it to show, and she continued, "I'll have to tell you about one of our surprises so you'll understand. A lot of mothers would like to help you if they just knew what to do. They don't really get the idea of Scouting if you don't let them help. Our first Leader thought up a great idea for the mothers, The Secret Buddy system. She had each Brownie choose a Secret Buddy, somebody's mother, and then they both wrote letters to each other and cards and stuff, and then in the fall, before the next year started, we had a party and invited all the mothers, and each one brought a ten cent present and gave it to her Secret Buddy. The best part of it was that the mothers didn't feel left out. They felt they were part of the Troop too. See? So we're going to do that at our picnic, only we're not going to tell you how, because you're not supposed to know about it. Promise you won't tell?"

I not only promised not to tell, I promised to reform. Next year I'd have just one Brownie Troop, I'd attend the Training Classes in the fall, I'd have a Troop Committee and mothers' meetings once a month. I'd invite mothers as guests to suggest new things to do, oh there were a whole lot of things I was going to do. "But Emily, I warn you now, if I find some children who don't have anywhere to go after school but sit on Vi's mourner's bench, I'm going to start another Troop—"

"Don't forget, I'll be in college," Emily said.

College! It seemed yesterday when Emily had first come to our door in her Brownie uniform saying, "Want to buy some Girl Scout Cookies?"

This time I hugged Emily and said both Jim and I prayed every night that our daughters would grow up to be exactly like her.

The day before, and the day of, the Great Big Family Picnic, the temperature at four o'clock in the afternoon was 80°. Emily and the Brownies were delirious with joy. They came bursting in after school and said there was another surprise for me. I wasn't to do one single thing for the picnic. I was to come down to the Park and just sit there, being waited on like a Princess. It would be just like a Court of Honor. Miss Dale and Miss Smith and Mrs. Blake and Mrs. Miller and I would be sitting on a decorated bench under the trees while they showed us what Girl Scouts can do. "We've got every single thing planned, Mrs. Jay. Every, single, solitary thing!"

Saturday afternoon at two o'clock Susan and Helen Miller and I met Miss Dale and Pat Smith just as we were entering the Park. From afar we could hear the cries of the seagulls and ducks mingled with the woodgatherers and cooks, as the Brownies scurried around preparing for the picnic.

Miss Dale took one look at this antlike activity and said, "You haven't one Leader to every six girls."

"No, but they've only been down here about fifteen minutes, and Emily and Judy and Jody are with them. What's more, at five o'clock every one of their mothers and fathers and heaven only knows how many relatives will arrive."

Pat Smith burst out laughing. "You never do things by halves, do you? Come on, let's go over and see what we can do to help."

I couldn't decide whether to admire Miss Dale or be jealous of her casual efficiency. She tossed one small log into the sullen Camp Stove and it blazed and turned bright red. We even had to put wet logs on it to keep the kettles of Campstew from burning. She showed us how to make a little cooler at the edge of the Lake out of driftwood tied together with reeds to keep the milk and lettuce cool. She was everywhere at once, followed by a string of admiring Brownies, and yet she was unhurried, calm and gracious.

Diana never left her side after she said water bugs were

called water striders because they seemed to stride on the surface of the water. "Actually they carry air on the surface of their bodies to use for respiration." As I saw their absorbed faces bent over the Lake watching the water striders, I had a distinct twinge of jealousy. I didn't want Diana to tell Miss Dale about bugs. I wanted her to tell me. Miss Dale already knew about bugs.

I looked up from staring enviously at Diana and Miss Dale, just in time to see May Chinn set off in a series of perfect cartwheels for the benefit of Pat Smith. It was somehow distressing to see a brown sparrow turning cartwheels when we were accustomed to watching a scarlet tanager, and it was even more distressing to have this exhibition produce two bloody noses and several bumped heads because my Pines and Firs also wished to show off for Pat Smith. While First Aid Kits were joyously produced by Susan's Maple and Alder to repair these injuries, argument waxing long and furious as to what to do in case of nosebleed, I walked over to the cookstove.

The cockles of my heart were instantly warmed by hearing my own Sally say, "Get Mommy to taste it. Mommy is the best cook in the whole world."

At four o'clock Emily said everything was ready and called the Leaders and Miss Dale and Miss Smith to sit down on the evergreen draped Honor Bench to await the Flying Up Ceremony. "Do you know your poem?" she whispered to me. I nodded, hoping I would not forget. Emily called the Patrols and they all marched over to the dressing rooms. We could hear gasps and giggles and "Is this right, Emily?" and "I can't find my cap, Judy" and "Jody, will you tie this?"

I was becoming more mournful by the minute. This was the last time I'd be able to watch Mari's grave little face as she and Phyllis seriously discussed plans for their Troop. Helen Miller was going to join Mrs. Burton's assistant and have their Scout Troop meetings in the basement of the church. Next fall Susan and Patty's mother, who was an ex-Scout Leader, were going to hold Sally's Troop meetings at her house. I wouldn't be able to watch Sally's blue eyes melting with tenderness as she helped me capture recalcitrant Pines and Firs. Next year, we wouldn't have "Patrols" —they were for Girl Scouts—Pat Smith had said so. Heidi probably never would be a Brownie, I'd made so many mistakes in handling her.

Miss Dale was regarding me with quizzical eyes as I sadly stared out over the Lake, counting my ex-Brownies like a rosary. She said, "I suspect you're finding it difficult to face giving up your Brownies—"

I nodded. "You become so attached to them—" I looked into her clear gray eyes and decided to tell the truth, the whole truth, and nothing but the truth. "I haven't been a good Leader, Miss Dale. I didn't realize it until I attended the Training Classes—"

Her eyes crinkled with amusement. "I'll admit that you haven't been an orthodox Leader, but you're more valuable than you realize. So many of our Leaders are unimaginative, afraid to try new things—'Handbook Happy' as the girls say. When in doubt, they fall back on entertainment—take the children to museums, zoos, theatres, always to observe rather than to participate. They do not employ the necessary imagination and patience to think up projects that Brownies can do. Experience has taught us that with a small, manageable group of children, ten to sixteen in a Troop, both the Leaders and the children gain more from Scouting. The rules we do insist on are made for the protection of the children. That's why we have the Training Classes, to explain our rules and the need for them."

I tried to express my real tenderness toward these Brownies, most of whom were unknown to me in September. "Actually I haven't gotten to know them all well, or as well as

I should have, and I might as well admit it. I don't like it when Diana talks bugs with you. I want Diana to tell *me* about her bugs."

She smiled slightly, her eyes kind and understanding. "It is difficult not to become too attached to them, but it makes it hard for them to go on through Scouting if their Leaders are not willing to give them up. In order to help them learn to work and play together so that they may grow up as responsible citizens of their community, it is necessary to learn to let them go. Perhaps that is one of the hardest things a Leader has to learn to do."

For the first time it occurred to me that perhaps Miss Dale's stern exterior was due to control rather than a lack of emotion. Perhaps she was afraid to show children how much she did like them. I remembered what Jim had said about women who became neurotic when their children grew up and left home.

Miss Dale continued, "Next year, you can begin with your second-grade Brownies. Then as you gain confidence, you can progress with them, and eventually you will all Fly Up and become Girl Scouts together. It's a satisfying and heart-warming experience, Mrs. Jay. Don't worry—just be yourself," she gave a sharp cry of laughter, "only not quite so much so. Here they come!"

Emily's full Senior Troop came marching down the field behind their Color Guard. White gloves, blue uniforms, as natty as a Troop of Waves. Behind them came Helen's Troop, their new green uniforms flicking from side to side. Behind them came Susan's Troop, eyes straight ahead, Brownie dresses crisp and perfect. Behind them came my Troop, straggly, giggling, and happy-go-lucky. Last of all came Heidi, followed by Spot and Dagmar.

I could barely see them as they formed two lines, the Scouts on one side, the Brownies on the other, and the dogs in the middle. Helen Miller stepped forward and began to give her Leader's Speech, the meaning of being a Brownie, being a Girl Scout, and Flying Up.

It was my turn to repeat the poem:

> "Brownies, you are just about
> To become true Girl Scouts.
> But when you have left the Pack
> Turn sometimes, and just look back;
> Remember that all Fairyland
> Really lies so close at hand.
> And if you're happy, brave and true
> You'll find the world all magic, too.
> In the Troop you soon will find
> Girl Scouts are loyal, clean and kind.
> And if you bring your Brownie grin
> And some Brownie magic in—
> The Troop, the town, the world and all
> Will like you even though you're small."

I probably would have broken down altogether had I not said, "Girl Scouts are loyal, clean and true," been prompted by Phyllis, "Girl Scouts are loyal, clean and kind," become hopelessly lost and had to start all over again. This time everybody was grinning.

Helen presented wings to each Flyer-Up and said,

> "So now I give you Brownie wings,
> That you may fly to Scoutly things."

and gave each of them the Scout Handshake.

As each of them stepped back, Emily's Seniors held out their hands and pulled them over to the Girl Scout line, saying:

> "Oh we're the Girl Scouts, a trusty band,
> And we welcome this elf from fairyland,
> We're ready to help her Lend a Hand
> So welcome, oh welcome, the Brownies!"

Then we all sang "Girl Scouts Together."

Promptly at five o'clock the families poured onto the playfield. Not only was there a hoard of mothers and fathers and sisters and cousins and aunts, there was also a constant undertow of small brothers and sisters who might have been a menace but, as fast as they arrived, they were whisked off by three Seniors, paper towels were stuffed in their necks, and they were lined up on the grass like strings of beads, fed appropriate portions of Campstew and Campcocoa, and promised ice cream cones if they sat still and ate every bit of their dinner.

Another group of Seniors lured the fathers and uncles and male guests off to play baseball against the brand new Intermediate Girl Scouts. Another group inveigled the Brownie Troops and older brothers and sisters to play Prisoner's Base.

This left the Honor Bench and an uneasy group of mothers and aunts, who had been invited to a picnic but told not to bring food, so there wasn't anything for them to do but sit there.

Emily came bounding over from the cooking area. "Why don't we use the Brownie system for getting acquainted. Just turn to the person next to you and say, 'What's your name? Where do you live? Which one is your Brownie?' " In ten minutes the various races, creeds and colors were chatting amicably on the one subject they all had in common—"my Brownie."

By the time our guests were seated at the long picnic table, their brilliant sport shirts and summer cottons as colorful as a zinnia bed, we were no longer strangers but neighbors, cemented together by the strongest bond in the world, our children. Vi and Murph, dressed alike for the occasion in rainbow striped denim jackets and gray denim slacks, produced shouts of laughter by "kidding the customers."

Susan's Troop, who had the honor of being "servers," were hovering in the background, filling plates with Campstew before they were empty. "Isn't this good? Have some more. We made it ourselves," spilling coffee impartially on laps and trousers and repeating, "Isn't this fun? Isn't this the best picnic you've ever been to?" and evoking knowing looks and proud chuckles.

Miss Dale and Pat Smith and Helen Miller were besieged to tell the mothers and fathers about Scout Camps. Their sales talk was so masterful that I found myself wishing I could go too.

The small undertow of babies kept breaking loose from their guardians and surging toward the parents, but were successfully stemmed each time by a seawall of ice cream cones.

The Lake was dappled with pink-tipped waves, the mountains were blue and lavender, even our Great White Father parted his clouds long enough to gaze down on the foolish families who planned a picnic without his permission and, seeing how genuinely happy they were, grew pink, then blue, then purple with content.

Emily came over to the long table and clapped her hands. "May we have your attention please. Would you mind turning around so you're facing the hillside?"

We turned around to see the Brownies, banked in six "Patrols." At a signal from Emily, they parted and there stood May Chinn in her scarlet Chinese dress, a flower-decked basket at her feet. Her satiny hair was brushed flat, she wore a golden circlet on her head with quivering scarlet flowers rising from it, her hands were folded demurely in her sleeves. She raised her lashes and slowly said, "Would one of you mothers like to be my Secret Buddy?" She paused and looked at each doting face. "Would you like to write me a letter? Brownies hardly ever get letters, and they like to get them just as much as you do." She picked up her basket. "In here I have every one of the Brownie names. I'll pass the basket and you draw a name. The name you draw is the name of your Secret Buddy." She hunched up her shoulders, giggled and put one golden finger to her lips. "One of you is already my Secret Buddy because we've already drawn your names. You probably think a Brownie is too little to keep a secret, but you'll find out."

There was a long drawn out "Oh-oh-oh-oh" of pure maudlin rapture as May Chinn began to flit up and down saying, "I wonder if I'll get a letter."

Susan sniffed and blew her nose. "If I hadn't watched that demon deliberately smear paste on Durdey's back, I'd be dripping tears on her first letter right now."

I asked Susan where on earth May had gotten her red Chinese dress; she was in uniform twenty minutes ago.

Susan murmured, "She calmly called up her grandfather and told him she was the only Brownie here without a mother and father and made him send her suitcase out in a taxi. She said she was going to make a speech about China. I went with her. I know."

May flashed back and stood peeking around the Brownies. "We wrote our birthdays down so you could send us a birthday card too, or a present!" "Good-bye, Secret Buddy—" And the Brownies closed ranks.

I found myself murmuring fatuously, "Bless her heart."

Then came the final heart-wringer, the giving of gifts. Not only was there a present for each parent, but for each aunt, uncle, Vi and Murph, Miss Dale and Pat Smith, Susan, Helen and me. Some of the fathers had to have their gifts explained to them. After all, you can't take one look and know that a board with six nails sticking crookedly in it is a tie rack. But by and large, every father and mother was flushed with pleasure.

For the guests, the Troops had drawn names and made an extra present, supervised by Emily, Judy and Jody. "So that's why they spent Tuesdays and Thursdays down in the gameroom," I thought as I untied my package and found a felt glasses case, with a card, "From your friend, Minnie, with love." I could barely see Minnie for tears as she stood in front of me. "Is the smoke from the stove getting in your eyes? Do you like it? I noticed you didn't have a glasses case."

I told her I loved it and loved her and hoped she'd come and see me in summer so she could help me take care of the garden. She said, "Sure, if you want me, I'd love it," and went tearing off. I looked up to see Susan, the mother hater, going from mother to mother, beaming, asking advice and being distinctly chummy as she explained that Brownies make their gifts out of the materials at hand.

She drew me aside. "Look at 'em. Bless their black hearts. It was worth it. Aren't they appreciative and really, darned nice?"

"Susan Blake. I thought you hated mothers," I said.

She grinned. "Wrong again. I hate interfering mothers. Take a look at the Storm Troopers."

Not for nothing had the Troop Committee spent years in clubs and organizations. Led by Mrs. Bean, they were stalking the mothers who did not work, chasing them relentlessly down their burrows, cornering them and shaking them until they signed up for a committee.

"Now look at the Council," Susan exulted.

Serene in the possession of a better mousetrap, Miss Dale and Pat Smith were sitting perfectly still on the bench of Honor, asking shrewd questions of the mothers who were fighting for the privilege of hurling themselves into Scouting.

"Leaders!" Susan rejoiced. "Assistant Leaders! By fall we won't have enough Brownies or Scouts to go around. Of course some of them will forget all about it when the glow of the picnic has worn off, but some of them are serious. Mrs. Lamson, Mrs. Rader, Colleen's Aunt Mollie—she's a natural—used to be a kindergarten teacher before she was married. Gloria's mother has invited us to have a meeting at the bakery and help the baker frost a cake, and Marcy's mother has offered to have a hairdressing party at the Beauty

Parlor, some of mine could use that, and Minnie's mother is going to arrange to have us visit the Airplane Factory—all three Troops." She grabbed my arm. "Come on, Sloughfoot, start dancing."

The Brownies clustered around their families, the mothers cradled sleepy babies, the Scouts made the Park "cleaner than when they found it" and the fathers gathered driftwood and built an enormous bonfire.

We sang and sang and sang. The fire blazed high as the treetops. Drowsy families snuggled together, their kindly faces reflected in the firelight as they sang nostalgic songs.

Jim put one arm around me and the other arm around his three daughters as we sang our farewell:

> "For all the glory of the Way
> For Thy protection night and day,
> For rooftree, fire, and bed, and board,
> For friends and home, we thank Thee, Lord."